KOREAN PICTURE DICTIONARY COLORING BOOK

Over 1500 Korean Words and Phrases
for Creative & Visual Learners of All Ages

Color and Learn

LingoMastery

ISBN-13: 978-1-951949-64-8

Free Book Reveals The 6 Step Blueprint That Took Students **<u>From Language Learners To Fluent In 3 Months</u>**

- **6 Unbelievable Hacks** that will accelerate your learning curve
- **Mind Training:** why memorizing vocabulary is easy
- **One Hack To Rule Them All:** This <u>secret nugget</u> will blow you away...

Head over to **<u>LingoMastery.com/hacks</u>** and claim your free book now!

CONTENTS

INTRODUCTION

Have you ever noticed that you can memorize something much better when you engage all your senses? This Korean Picture Dictionary Coloring Book is designed to help you build the Korean vocabulary in an efficient way that you can use your different senses. It covers a wide range of topics from members of the family and animals to parts of the body and describing jobs.

This introduction is a guide to help you get started in Korean and polish your basic grammar, spelling, and vocabulary skills. You can also have a glimpse of the differences between English and Korean in many ways. Welcome to the journey of Korean mastery! Enjoy yourself!

BASICS OF THE KOREAN LANGUAGE

I. Hangul, the Korean alphabet

a. Letters

Hangul is similar to the English alphabet since each letter represents a different sound, but sometimes the letter sound changes depending on the word or the way the word is used. And just as English, Hangul is written left to right.

Modern Hangul orthography uses 24 basic letters:

- 14 simple consonants (ㄱ,ㄴ,ㄷ,ㄹ,ㅁ,ㅂ,ㅅ,ㅇ,ㅈ,ㅊ,ㅋ,ㅌ,ㅍ,ㅎ)
- 5 double consonant letters (ㄲ,ㄸ,ㅃ,ㅆ,ㅉ)
- 11 compound consonant letters (ㄳ,ㄵ,ㄶ,ㄺ,ㄻ,ㄼ,ㄽ,ㄾ,ㄿ,ㅀ,ㅄ)
- 10 simple vowels (ㅏ,ㅑ,ㅓ,ㅕ,ㅗ,ㅛ,ㅜ,ㅠ,ㅡ,ㅣ)
- 11 compound vowel letters (ㅐ,ㅒ,ㅔ,ㅖ,ㅘ,ㅙ,ㅚ,ㅝ,ㅞ,ㅟ,ㅢ)

	Letter	Name*	Sound Value
Simple Consonants	ㄱ	기역 (gi-yeok)	[g] or [k]
	ㄴ	니은 (ni-eun)	[n]
	ㄷ	디귿 (di-geut)	[d] or [t]
	ㄹ	리을 (ri-eul)	[r] or [l]
	ㅁ	미음 (mi-eum)	[m]
	ㅂ	비읍 (bi-eup)	[b] or [p]
	ㅅ	시옷 (shi-ot)	[s] or [sh]
	ㅇ	이응 (i-eung)	[ng]

	ㅈ	지읒 (ji-eut)	[dʒ]
	ㅊ	치읓 (chi-eut)	[ch] or [tʃʰ]
	ㅋ	키읔 (ki-euk)	[k] or [kʰ]
	ㅌ	티읕 (ti-eut)	[t] or [tʰ]
	ㅍ	피읖 (pi-eup)	[p] or [pʰ]
	ㅎ	히읗 (hi-eut)	[h]
Double Consonants	ㄲ	쌍기역 (ssang-gi-yeok)	[kk] or [k′]
	ㄸ	쌍디귿 (ssang-di-geut)	[tt] or [t′]
	ㅃ	쌍비읍 (ssang-bi-eup)	[pp] or [p′]
	ㅆ	쌍시옷 (ssang-shi-ot)	[ss] or [s′]
	ㅉ	쌍지읒 (ssang-ji-eut)	[jj] or [tʃ′]
Simple Vowels	ㅏ	아 (a)	[a]
	ㅑ	야 (ya)	[ya]
	ㅓ	어 (eo)	[eo]
	ㅕ	여 (yeo)	[yeo]
	ㅗ	오 (o)	[o]
	ㅛ	요 (yo)	[yo]
	ㅜ	우 (u)	[u]
	ㅠ	유 (yu)	[yu]
	ㅡ	으 (eu)	[eu]
	ㅣ	이 (i)	[i:]
Compound Vowels	ㅐ	애 (ae)	[æ]
	ㅒ	얘 (yae)	[yɛ] or [ye]
	ㅔ	에 (e)	[e]
	ㅖ	예 (ye)	[yɛ] or [ye]

	ㅘ	와 (wa)	[wa]
	ㅙ	왜 (wae)	[we]
	ㅚ	외 (oe)	[we]
	ㅝ	워 (wo)	[wə]
	ㅞ	웨 (we)	[we]
	ㅟ	위 (wi)	[wi]
	ㅢ	의 (ui)	[ui]

*The transcriptions in the parentheses are IPA transcriptions according to the Romanization rule of Korean.

ATTENTION:

- The 11 compound consonant letters do not have their own alphabet names, and their pronunciations are irregular.
- The simple vowel 'ㅡ' is not exactly marked in English words, as it works as a passing sound. i.e. tree [teu-ri:], black [beu-læk], sky [seu-kai:]
- ㅋ, ㅌ, ㅍ, ㅊ are called aspirated sounds, so please compare the pronunciations of ㄱ and ㅋ (ㄱ with aspiration), ㄷ and ㅌ (ㄷ with aspiration), ㅂ and ㅍ (ㅂ with aspiration), ㅈ and ㅊ (ㅈ with aspiration).
- ㄲ, ㄸ, ㅃ, ㅆ, ㅉ are called tense sounds, so please compare the pronunciations of ㄱ and ㄲ, ㄷ and ㄸ, ㅂ and ㅃ, ㅅ and ㅆ, ㅈ and ㅉ carefully.
- Current speakers of standard Korean do not differentiate between the vowels ㅐ and ㅔ (Koreans do not distinguish [æ] and [e] nowadays), ㅒ and ㅖ (both are pronounced as [ye]) in pronunciation. Also, ㅙ, ㅞ, and ㅚ are all pronounced as [we].
- There is no equivalent pronunciation of 'ㅢ' in English. You can start pronouncing 'ㅡ' first, and then slide to pronouncing 'ㅣ'. 'ㅡ' should be shorter than 'ㅣ'.

b. How to form each character

Each Hangul character is a syllabic block made up of both consonants and vowels. Syllables are mostly made up according to the CVC (consonant + vowel + consonant) structure, and when there is no initial consonant, we use 'ㅇ' as a filler, whereas we leave the third place empty when there is no final consonant. There are two different locations for vowels; one is vertical for ㅏ, ㅑ, ㅓ, ㅕ, ㅣ, and the other is horizontal for ㅗ, ㅛ, ㅜ, ㅠ, ㅡ. The ordering of consonants and vowels is indicated below.

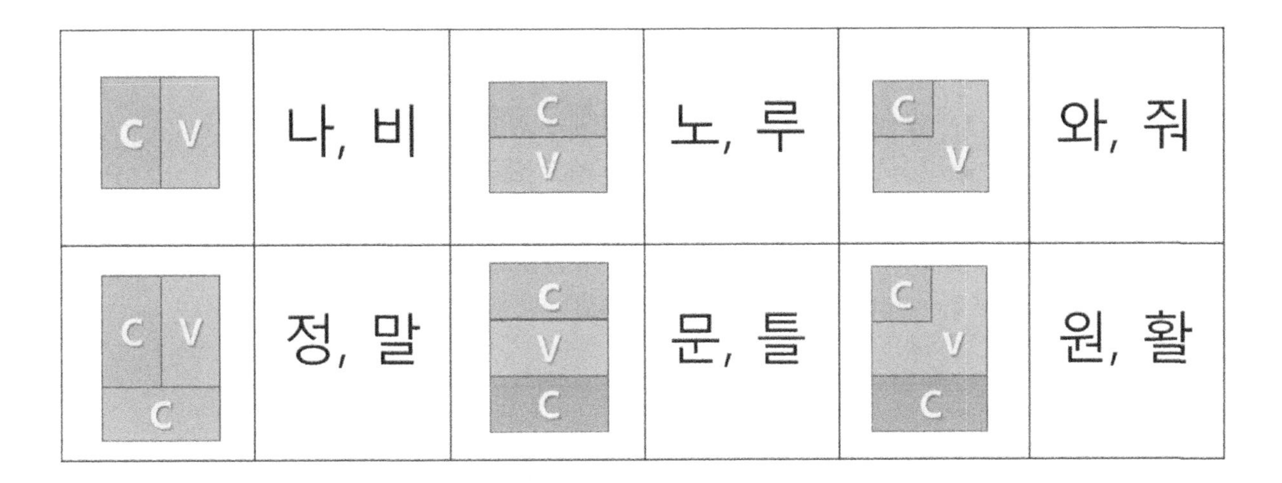

C V	나, 비	C V	노, 루	C V	와, 줘
C V C	정, 말	C V C	문, 틀	C V C	원, 활

II. The Characteristics of Korean Grammar

a. Word order

1. In Korean, the basic order of the sentence is as follows: Subject – Object – Verb (SOV).

e.g. 클레어 씨가 한국어를 공부해요. (Claire studies Korean.) (Subject) (Object) (Verb)

2. While the word-order is grammatically rigid in English, it is relatively flexible in Korean grammar. In terms of the word-order, English is a position-dependent language, but Korean is a function-dependent language. We can understand how each part of the Korean sentence functions by looking at markers (particles) and verb endings (conjugation).

e.g. 클레어 씨가 요즘 한국어를 공부해요. (Claire studies Korean.)
(Subject) (Adverb) (Object) (Verb)

It is also acceptable to say:

- 요즘 클레어 씨가 한국어를 공부해요.
- 클레어 씨가 한국어를 요즘 공부해요.
- 요즘 한국어를 클레어 씨가 공부해요.
- 한국어를 요즘 클레어 씨가 공부해요.
- 한국어를 클레어 씨가 요즘 공부해요.
- 클레어 씨가 한국어를 공부해요 요즘.
- 한국어를 클레어 씨가 공부해요 요즘.

3. When forming a question, neither the question word (who, what, etc.) nor the other parts of the sentence are moved around.

e.g.

누가 클레어 씨를 만났어요? (Who met Claire?)

유민 씨가 누구를 만났어요? (Whom did Yumin meet?)

유민 씨가 클레어 씨를 언제 만났어요? (When did Yumin meet Claire?)

유민 씨가 클레어 씨를 왜 만났어요? (Why did Yumin meet Claire?)

b. Markers (particles)

1. Markers refer to the grammatical endings that you attach at the end of nouns to indicate what their function is in the sentence. For example, in the sentence below, '-가' indicates that '클레어 씨' is acting as the subject of the sentence, and '-를' indicates that '한국어' is acting as the object of the sentence. In addition to these markers, there are also many others used in Korean, including '-에', '-에서', '-으로', '-은/는'.

e.g. 클레어 씨가 한국어를 공부해요.
(클레어 씨 + -가) (한국어 + -를)

Below are some of the most common markers in Korean.

(1) 은 and 는: topic markers to indicate what is being talked about in a sentence.

(2) 이 and 가: subject markers to indicate the subject of the sentence.

(3) 을 and 를: object markers to indicate the object of the sentence.

(4) 와, 과, 하고, 랑, 이랑: linking markers that are equivalent to 'and' in English.

(5) 의: a possessive marker that expresses the owner of the following noun.

(6) 에 and 에서: usually attached at the end of the nouns indicating places or time.

(7) 으로 and 로: used to indicate destinations or tools that are used, etc.

2. In conversation, the markers are often left out of the sentence. This is especially the case with information that both the speaker and listener are well aware of.

e.g.
A: 오늘 날씨(가) 어때? (What's the weather like today?)
B: 오늘 날씨(는) 정말 좋아. (Today's weather is very good.)

A: 난 오늘 서울(에) 가서 친구(를) 만날 거야. (I'm going to Seoul to meet up with my friend.)
B: 그럼 지하철(을) 타고 가니? (Then, are you going to take the subway?)

c. **Verb endings (conjugation)**

1. Unlike English, verbs do not have to agree with the subject in number and person.

2. In Korean, adjectives act a lot like verbs. In fact, an adjective at the end of the sentence usually looks just like a verb. Unlike English, you do not need to use a verb like 'be' with adjectives.

> e.g. 클레어 씨의 강아지는 작아요. (Claire's puppy is small.)
> (작- + -아요)

3. The basic form of verbs ends with '-다'. Verb endings are placed immediately after a verb or adjective and provide the following information:

(1) Tense: whether the sentence takes places in the past, present, or future.

(2) Honorifics: whether the subject of the sentence or the listener is of higher social status than the speaker.

(3) Formality: whether the conversation is taking place in a formal setting or not.

(4) Mood: whether the sentence is a statement, question, command, or suggestion. (For more information about honorifics and formality, please refer to the end of this guide.)

For example, in the next sentence, the '-어요' which is affixed to the end of the verb '읽-' (to read) communicates the following information:

> e.g. 클레어 씨가 책을 읽어요? (Does Claire read a book?)
> (읽- + -어요)
>
> (1) Tense: Claire is reading a book in the present.
>
> (2) Honorifics: Claire is not of a higher social status than the speaker.
>
> (3) Formality: This conversation is an example of informal polite speech.
>
> (4) Mood: The speaker is asking a question – whether Claire is reading a book.

The tables below show some of the common verb endings in Korean.

Tense				
	과거 (Past)	-었- -었었-		클레어 씨가 책을 읽었다. 클레어 씨가 책을 읽었었다.
	현재 (Present)	동사 (Verb)	-는/ㄴ-	클레어 씨가 책을 읽는다. 클레어 씨가 책을 읽는구나. 클레어 씨가 책을 읽어.
		형용사 (Adjective)	X	클레어 씨는 예쁘다.
	미래 (Future)	-겠- -을 것이-		클레어 씨는 책을 읽을 것이다.

			Mood				
Formality	**Honorifics**		평서문 (Declarative Sentence)	의문문 (Interrogative Sentence)	명령문 (Imperative Sentence)	청유문 (Request Sentence)	감탄문 (Exclamatory Sentence)
비격식체 (Informal)	Casual	해체	비가 내려.	언제 귀국해?	어서 가.	책을 읽어.	정말 반가워.
	Polite	해요체	비가 내려요.	언제 귀국해요?	어서 가세요.	책을 읽어요.	정말 반가워요.
격식체 (Formal)	Casual	해라체	비가 내리다.	언제 귀국하니?	어서 가라.	책을 읽자.	정말 반갑구나.
		하게체	비가 내리네.	언제 귀국하는가?	어서 가게.	책을 읽게.	정말 반갑구만.
	Polite	하오체	비가 내리오.	언제 귀국하시오?	어서 가시오.	책을 읽읍시다.	정말 반갑구려.
		하십시오체	비가 내립니다.	언제 귀국하십니까?	어서 가십시오.	책을 읽으시지요.	

4. In English, the verb 'to be' always appears by itself in the sentence. But in Korean, '-이다' can be attached directly to the end of a noun. It should be also noted that '-이다' can change like a verb as we have explained. Let's look at the following example.

   e.g. 클레어 씨는 학생이다. (Claire is a student.)
   (학생 + -이다)

5. The way to address someone depends on the speaker's relationship to the person being addressed and the level of formality. In other words, when making a sentence in Korean, you have to consider the relationship between the subject of the sentence and the speaker, including who is older, who holds a higher social rank, and how close they are. Of course, the same considerations apply to the relationship between the speaker and the listener.

   e.g. Claire goes to school.

   클레어 씨가 학교에 가요. (Claire ≤ the speaker, the listener ≥ the speaker)

   클레어 씨가 학교에 가세요. (Claire > the speaker, the listener ≥ the speaker)

   In addition, it's also important to know whether the setting of the conversation is formal or not.

   e.g. Claire goes to school.

   클레어 씨가 학교에 가요. → in informal polite speech

   클레어 씨가 학교에 가세요. → in formal polite speech

III. The Characteristics of Korean Vocabulary

1. A lot of Korean words derived from Chinese, but they are written in Hangul. This is why words with the same Hangul can mean different things. For example, 부자 can mean 'the rich' as well as 'a father and a son,' since their Chinese characters are different whereas their Korean pronunciation is the same. Despite word borrowing, Korean is completely distinct from Chinese in sound and in sentence structure.

   Below are some of the examples:

Word	Chinese character	English meaning
부자	富者	the rich, the wealthy
	父子	father and son
의사	醫師	medical doctor
	意思	mind, intention
이성	理性	reason, the capacity to think and judge logically
	異性	the opposite sex
자비	慈悲	mercy, compassion
	自費	one's own expense, self-financing
전기	電氣	electricity
	傳記	biography
사고	事故	accident, trouble
	思考	thought, thinking, contemplation
수입	輸入	import
	收入	earning, income, revenue
수도	首都	capital city
	水道	water supply, waterworks
동기	動機	motive
	同氣	sibling
장관	長官	minister, the head of a government ministry
	壯觀	spectacle, scene

2. Korean is a language that has highly developed onomatopoeic or mimetic words, which mean the words that imitate sounds or motions. For example, 'yellow' in English can be translated into '노랗다', '누렇다', '누리끼리하다', '노르스름하다', '노릇노릇하다', to name but a few, and their connotations are slightly different. There are scores of other expressions for 'yellow', and can be largely flexible according to regions, speakers, etc.

   Below are some of the examples of Korean onomatopoeic and mimetic words:

English meaning	Korean words
Short, quivering sound	부르릉, 드르륵, 다르륵, 따르릉, 드르렁, 찌르르르, 으르릉, 으르렁, 끄르륵, 좌르륵, 주르륵, 후르룩, 스르륵, 와르르르, 갸르릉
Bubbling of boiling water	부글부글, 보글보글, 뽀글뽀글, 바글바글, 버글버글, 빠글빠글, 뿌글뿌글
Red	빨갛다, 벌겋다, 새빨갛다, 시뻘겋다, 발그래하다, 붉다, 불그래하다, 불긋불긋하다, 불그스름하다
Yellow	노랗다, 누렇다, 샛노랗다, 누리끼리하다, 노르스름하다, 노릇노릇하다, 노르께하다
Blue	파랗다, 퍼렇다, 새파랗다, 시퍼렇다, 파릇파릇하다, 푸르스름하다
Crowded	우글우글, 와글와글, 드글드글, 득시글득시글, 북적북적, 복작복작
Open mouth with smile	헤, 헤헤, 헤벌레, 헤벌쭉, 헤롱헤롱, 헬렐레, 헤죽헤죽, 헤실헤실
Ripply or brimful	찰랑찰랑, 철푸덕, 철퍽철퍽, 철벙철벙, 첨벙첨벙, 찰싹, 착

3. In addition to varying verb endings for honorific expressions, different words are used to show respect to others. Those words often look unrelated to each other, but can indicate the same thing. Knowing how to address properly in Korean conversations is regarded very important, so it is recommended to keep in mind that there are casual and honorific expressions for same things especially for commonly used items or motions. For example, 밥 means a meal for casual situations, but for seniors, 진지, the honorific equivalent of 밥 is used to show respect.

Below are some of the examples:

	English meaning	Casual	Honorific
Nouns Pronouns	I	나	저
	We / our / us	우리	저희
	Name	이름	성함
	House	집	댁
	Age	나이	연세
	Birthday	생일	생신
Verbs Adjectives	To be / to exist	있다	계시다
	To sleep	자다	주무시다
	To eat	먹다	잡수시다, 드시다
	To give	주다	드리다
	To be sick	아프다	편찮으시다
	To ask	묻다	여쭙다
	To talk / to speak / to say	말하다	말씀하다
	To be hungry	배고프다	시장하시다

4. Korean uses long and short vowel sounds to distinguish the meaning of some words. This is one of the reasons why the same written word can indicate many different thin gs. For example, 눈 can mean two different things, eyes and snow. However, for eyes, ㅜ of 눈 sounds shorter, and for snow, it is pronounced longer than 눈 for eyes.

   Below are some of the examples of the vowel length distinction:

Written word	Sound	English meaning
눈	눈	snow
	눈:	eyes
말	말	horses
	말:	speech, word, language
밤	밤	night, evening
	밤:	chestnut
병	병	bottle
	병:	disease
사과	사과	apple
	사:과	apology
적다	적다	to write down
	적:다	to be little, a little
묻다	묻다	to bury
	묻:다	to ask, to inquire

5. The use of -들 as a marker of plurality in Korean is quite common in discourse; thus, it is roughly equivalent to plural '-s' in English. However, -들 is not used as often as in English, and the plural marker is left out more frequently for objects than for people.

> e.g.
>
> I've got a book and a pencil.
>
> I've got books and pencils.
>
> ➔ Both can be translated into
>
> 책과 연필이 있어요. (rather than 책들과 연필들이 있어요.)

TIPS ON TRANSLITERATION

Throughout this book you can find the transliteration added to each word to help you pronounce them correctly. Here are some of the tips on how you should read them.

1. The transliterations are mostly written according to the Romanization rule set by the National Institute of Korean Language (Republic of Korea). The table below shows the summary of the Romanization rule. Some transliterations may not exactly reflect the real pronunciation.

ㅏ	ㅓ	ㅗ	ㅜ	ㅡ	ㅣ	ㅐ	ㅔ	ㅚ	ㅟ
a	eo	o	u	eu	i	ae	e	oe	wi

ㅑ	ㅕ	ㅛ	ㅠ	ㅒ	ㅖ	ㅘ	ㅙ	ㅝ	ㅞ	ㅢ
ya	yeo	yo	yu	yae	ye	wa	wae	wo	we	ui

ㄱ	ㄲ	ㅋ	ㄷ	ㄸ	ㅌ	ㅂ	ㅃ	ㅍ
g, k	kk	k	d, t	tt	t	b, p	pp	p

ㅈ	ㅉ	ㅊ	ㅅ	ㅆ	ㅎ	ㄴ	ㅁ	ㅇ	ㄹ
j	jj	ch	s	ss	h	n	m	ng	r, l

2. When the sound values change according to the preceding or following characters, the results of those changes are transcribed.
   i.e. 깨끗하다 → kka-**kkeu-ta**-da (kka-**kkeut-ha**-da X), 담요 → dam-**nyo** (dam-**yo** X)

3. Considering the possibility of confusion in pronunciation, hyphens are added between syllables. However, the words with liaison syllables are separated by hyphen according to the pronunciation, and not according to the written characters.

i.e. 불안하다 → **bu-ran**-ha-da (**bul-an**-ha-da X)

비슷하다 → bi-**seu-ta**-da (bi-**seut-ha**-da X)

4. For the words whose Korean pronunciations are very similar to those of English, we write English words in Italic fonts. Note, however, that *Koreanized* pronunciations of some words borrowed from English are written according to the Romanization rule. And also, Koreans do not usually pronounce 's' at the end of a word.

   i.e. 생강 쿠키 → saeng-gang ***cookie***

   범퍼카 (bumper **cars**) → *bumper* ***car***

5. Spaces are put in the transliterations according to the original Korean words. In that case, we do not add hyphens to separate the pronunciation.

   i.e. 곰 인형 → gom in-hyeong

   휴대 전화 → hyu-dae jeon-hwa

감정 (EMOTIONS)

1) **기쁘다** (happy)
gi-ppeu-da

2) **슬프다** (sad)
seul-peu-da

3) **신나다** (excited)
shin-nan-da

4) **화나다** (angry)
hwa-na-da

5) **놀라다** (surprised)
nol-la-da

6) **걱정되다** (concerned)
geok-jeong-doe-da

7) **무섭다** (scared)
mu-seop-da

8) **호기심이 많다** (curious)
ho-gi-shi-mi man-ta

9) **즐겁다** (amused)
jeul-geop-da

10) **헷갈리다** (confused)
het-gal-li-da

11) **아프다** (sick)
a-peu-da

12) **버릇없다** (naughty)
beo-reu-deop-da

13) **진지하다** (serious)
jin-ji-ha-da

14) **집중하다** (focused)
jip-jung-ha-da

15) **지루하다** (bored)
ji-ru-ha-da

16) **압도되다** (overwhelmed)
ap-do-doe-da

17) **사랑하다** (in love)
sa-rang-ha-da

18) **부끄럽다** (ashamed)
bu-kkeu-reop-da

19) **불안하다** (anxious)
bu-ran-ha-da

20) **역겹다** (disgusted)
yeok-gyeop-da

21) **불쾌하다** (offended)
bul-kwe-ha-da

22) **쓰리다** (sore)
sseu-ri-da

그는 당신에게 화났어요.
He is angry at you.

우리 조부모님은 아직도 서로를 정말 사랑하세요.
My grandparents are still very much in love.

그녀의 미소는 언제나 나를 기쁘게 해.
Her smile always makes me happy.

1
2
3
4
5
6
7
8
9
10
11
12
13
14
15
16
17
18
19
20
21
22

가족 (THE FAMILY)

1) **조부모님** (grandparents)
jo-bu-mo-nim

2) **할머니** (grandmother)
hal-meo-ni

3) **할아버지** (grandfather)
ha-ra-beo-ji

4) **삼촌, 고모부, 이모부** (uncle)
sam-chon, go-mo-bu, i-mo-bu

5) **엄마, 어머니** (mother)
eom-ma, eo-meo-ni

6) **아빠, 아버지** (father)
a-ppa, a-beo-ji

7) **고모, 이모, 숙모** (aunt)
go-mo, i-mo, sung-mo

8) **사촌** (cousin, m.)
sa-chon

9) **형, 오빠, 남동생** (brother)
hyeong, o-ppa, nam-dong-saeng

10) **나, 저** (me)
na, jeo

11) **남편 / 아내** (husband/wife)
nam-pyeon, a-nae

12) **누나, 언니, 여동생** (sister)
nu-na, eon-ni, yeo-dong-saeng

13) **사촌** (first cousin)
sa-chon

14) **조카** (nephew, niece)
jo-ka

15) **아들** (son)
a-deul

16) **딸** (daughter)
Ddal

17) **조카** (niece)
jo-ka

18) **손자** (grandson)
son-ja

19) **손녀** (granddaughter)
son-nyeo

20) **육촌** (second cousin)
yuk-chon

- **인척 (in-laws) – 친척 (relatives)**

in-cheok – chin-cheok

21) **시아버지, 장인** (father-in-law)
shi-a-beo-ji, jang-in

22) **시어머니, 장모** (mother-in-law)
shi-eo-meo-ni, jang-mo

23) **시동생, 처남, 매형** (brother-in-law)
shi-dong-saeng, cheo-nam, mae-hyeong

24) **시누이, 올케, 처제, 처형** (sister-in-law)
shi-nu-i, ol-ke, cheo-je, cheo-hyeong

25) **며느리** (daughter-in-law)
myeo-neu-ri

26) **사위** (son-in-law)
sa-wi

27) **고모부, 이모부** (uncle-in-law)
go-mo-bu, i-mo-bu

28) **고모, 이모, 숙모** (aunt-in-law)
go-mo, i-mo, sung-mo

우리 사위가 자주 집에 필요한 일들을 도와준다.
My son-in-law often helps me around the house.

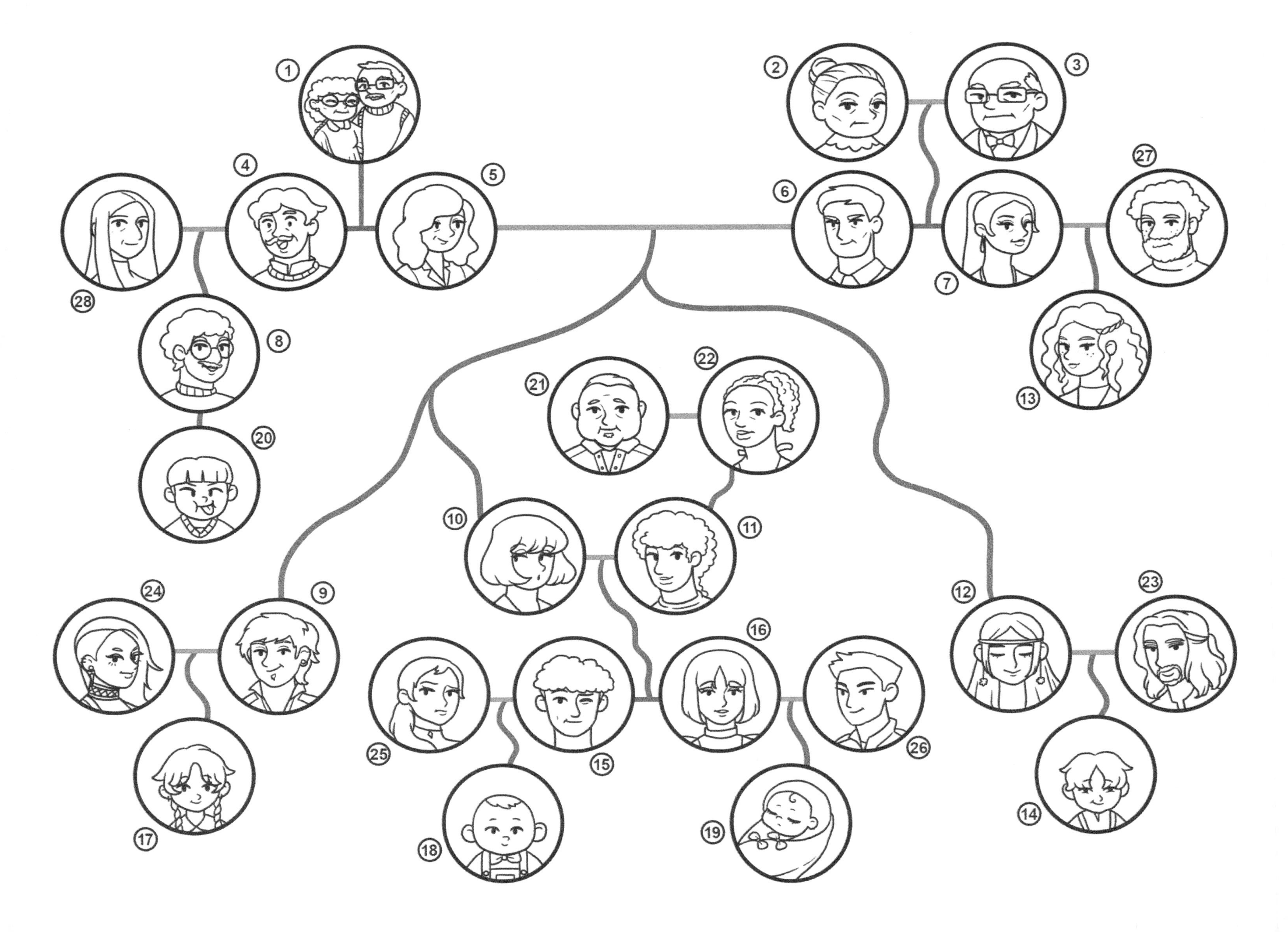
1
2
3
4
5
6
7
8
9
10
11
12
13
14
15
16
17
18
19
20
21
22
23
24
25
26
27
28

관계 (RELATIONSHIPS)

1) **부부** (married couple)
bu-bu

2) **유부남** (married man)
yu-bu-nam

3) **유부녀** (married woman)
yu-bu-nyeo

4) **이혼 부부** (divorced couple)
i-hon bu-bu

5) **전부인** (ex-wife)
jeon-bu-in

6) **전남편** (ex-husband)
jeon-nam-pyeon

7) **친구** (friend)
chin-gu

8) **여자친구** (girlfriend)
yeo-ja-chin-gu

9) **남자친구** (boyfriend)
nam-ja-chin-gu

10) **이웃** (neighbor)
i-ut

11) **독신** (single)
dok-shin

12) **이혼녀 / 이혼남** (divorcée/divorcé)
i-hon-nyeo / i-hon-nam

13) **홀아비** (widower)
ho-ra-bi

14) **과부** (widow)
gwa-bu

에디는 새로운 여자친구가 생겼습니다.
Eddie has a new girlfriend.

저는 작년부터 독신이에요.
I have been single since last year.

내 이웃은 정말 호기심이 많다.
My neighbor is very curious.

①
②
③
④
⑤
⑥
⑦
⑧
⑨
⑩
⑪
⑫
⑬
⑭

가치관 (VALUES)

1) **존경** (respect)
jon-gyeong
2) **감사** (gratitude)
gam-sa
3) **관용** (tolerance)
gwa-nyong
4) **협동** (collaboration)
hyeop-dong
5) **정직** (honesty)
jeong-jik
6) **절제** (temperance)
jeol-je
7) **책임** (responsibility)
chae-gim
8) **믿음** (faith)
mi-deum
9) **용기** (courage)
yong-gi
10) **친절** (kindness)
chin-jeol
11) **헌신** (commitment)
heon-shin
12) **열정** (enthusiasm)
yeol-jeong
13) **신뢰** (trust)
shil-loe
14) **시간 엄수** (punctuality)
shi-gan eom-su

그 회사는 시간 엄수에 대해 매우 엄격하다.
The company is very strict on punctuality.

나는 당신을 신뢰한다.
I trust you.

나는 직장에서 많은 책임을 지고 있다.
I have a lot of responsibilities at work.

인체 (THE HUMAN BODY)

1) **머리** (head)
   meo-ri
2) **머리카락** (hair)
   meo-ri-ka-rak
3) **얼굴** (face)
   eol-gul
4) **이마** (forehead)
   i-ma
5) **귀** (ear)
   gwi
6) **눈** (eyes)
   nun
7) **코** (nose)
   ko
8) **볼** (cheek)
   bol
9) **입** (mouth)
   ip
10) **턱** (chin)
    teok
11) **목** (neck)
    mok
12) **등** (back)
    deung
13) **가슴** (chest)
    ka-seum
14) **어깨** (shoulder)
    eo-kkae
15) **팔** (arm)
    pal
16) **팔뚝** (forearm)
    pal-ttuk
17) **손** (hand)
    son
18) **배** (abdomen)
    bae
19) **허리** (waist)
    heo-ri
20) **엉덩이** (hip)
    eong-deong-i
21) **다리** (leg)
    da-ri
22) **허벅지** (thigh)
    heo-beok-ji
23) **무릎** (knee)
    mu-reup
24) **종아리** (calf)
    jong-a-ri
25) **정강이** (shin)
    jeong-gang-i
26) **발** (foot)
    bal

나는 일곱 살 때 팔이 부러졌어.
I broke my arm when I was 7.

너는 아직도 등이 아파?
Does your back still hurt?

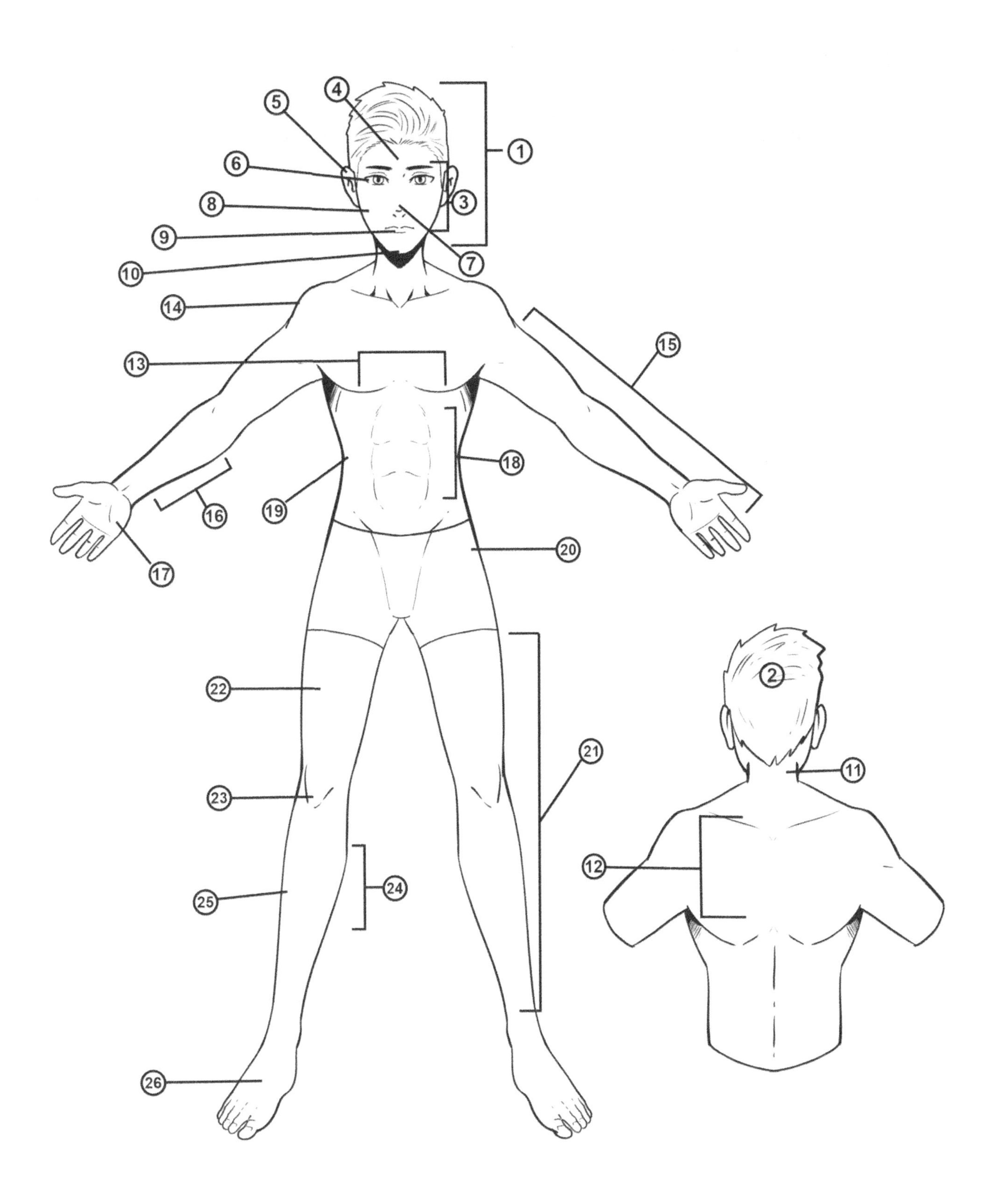

1
2
3
4
5
6
7
8
9
10
11
12
13
14
15
16
17
18
19
20
21
22
23
24
25
26

인체 내부 (INSIDE THE HUMAN BODY)

1) **피부** (skin)
   pi-bu
2) **근육** (muscles)
   geu-nyuk
3) **뼈** (bones)
   ppyeo
4) **뇌** (brain)
   noe
5) **갑상선** (thyroid)
   gap-sang-seon
6) **정맥** (veins)
   jeong-maek
7) **동맥** (arteries)
   dong-maek
8) **심장** (heart)
   shim-jang
9) **폐** (lungs)
   pye
10) **위장** (stomach)
    wi-jang
11) **식도** (esophagus)
    shik-do
12) **췌장** (pancreas)
    chew-jang
13) **간** (liver)
    kan
14) **소장** (small intestine)
    so-jang
15) **대장** (large intestine)
    dae-jang
16) **담낭** (gallbladder)
    dam-nang
17) **신장** (kidneys)
    shin-jang
18) **방광** (urinary bladder)
    bang-gwang

저는 신장 수술을 받았어요.
I had an operation on my kidneys.

흡연은 폐에 나쁘다.
Smoking is bad for the lungs.

카페인은 뼈를 약하게 한다.
Caffeine can make your bones weak.

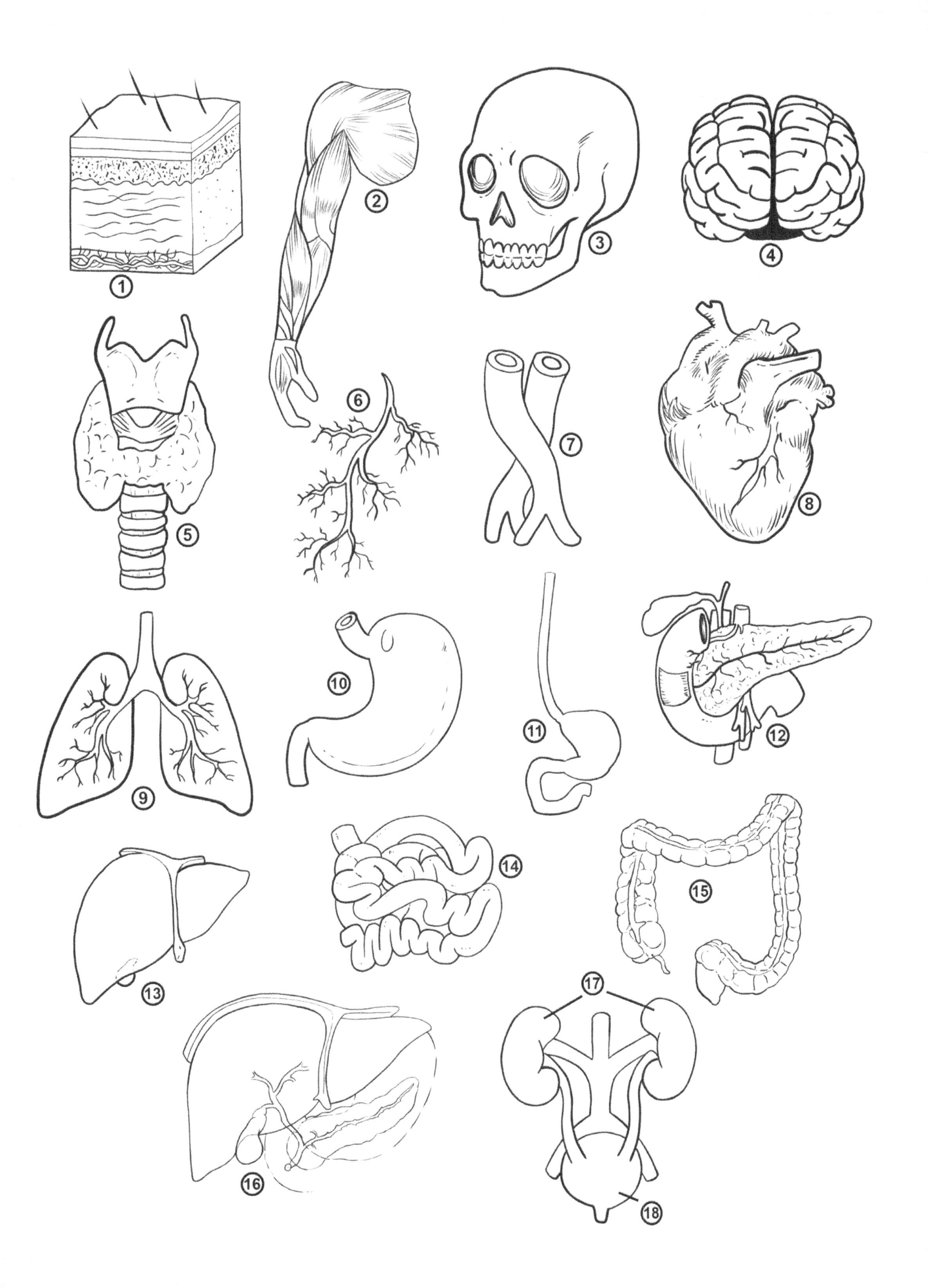
1
2
3
4
5
6
7
8
9
10
11
12
13
14
15
16
17
18

반려동물 (PETS)

1) **개** (dog)
gae
2) **고양이** (cat)
go-yang-i
3) **페럿** (ferret)
ferret
4) **미니 돼지** (mini pig/teacup pig)
mini-dwae-ji
5) **말** (horse)
mal
6) **에인절 피시** (angelfish)
angelfish
7) **흰동가리** (clown fish)
huin-dong-ga-ri
8) **금붕어** (goldfish)
geum-bung-eo
9) **햄스터** (hamster)
hamster
10) **기니피그** (guinea pig)
guinea pig
11) **쥐** (mouse)
jwi
12) **토끼** (rabbit)
to-kki
13) **고슴도치** (hedgehog)
ko-seum-do-chi
14) **타란툴라** (tarantula)
tarantula
15) **개미떼** (ant colony)
gae-mi-tte
16) **거북이** (tortoise)
keo-bu-gi
17) **뱀** (snake)
baem
18) **카멜레온** (chameleon)
chameleon
19) **이구아나** (iguana)
iguana
20) **카나리아** (canary)
ka-na-ri-a
21) **앵무새** (parrot)
aeng-mu-sae
22) **잉꼬** (parakeet)
ing-kko

나는 고양이보다 강아지가 더 좋아.
I prefer dogs over cats.

난 우리 딸한테 금붕어를 선물했다.
I gifted a goldfish to my daughter.

우리는 거북이를 기르고 있어요.
We have tortoises.

22
21
16
12
14
1
13
15
18
19
20
6
17
4
8
3
7
10
9
2
5
11

동물원 (THE ZOO)

1) **코끼리** (elephant)
ko-kki-ri

2) **코뿔소** (rhino)
Ko-ppul-so

3) **기린** (giraffe)
ki-rin

4) **얼룩말** (zebra)
eol-lung-mal

5) **하마** (hippopotamus)
ha-ma

6) **치타** (cheetah)
cheetah

7) **호랑이** (tiger)
ho-rang-i

8) **사자** (lion)
sa-ja

9) **침팬지** (chimpanzee)
chimpanzee

10) **오랑우탄** (orangutan)
orangutan

11) **개코원숭이** (baboon)
gae-ko-won-sung-i

12) **캥거루** (kangaroo)
kangaroo

13) **코알라** (koala)
koala

14) **여우원숭이** (lemur)
yeo-u-won-sung-i

사자는 동물의 왕입니다.
The lion is the king of animals.

나 호주에서 코알라 만져봤어.
I petted a koala in Australia.

코끼리는 정말 똑똑해요.
Elephants are very intelligent.

13
8
14
12
9
7
11
10
6
5
3
4
1
2

새 (BIRDS)

1) **타조** (ostrich)
ta-jo
2) **공작새** (peacock)
kong-jak-sae
3) **칠면조** (turkey)
chil-myeon-jo
4) **수탉, 닭** (rooster)
su-tak, dak
5) **오리** (duck)
o-ri
6) **백조** (swan)
baek-jo
7) **펠리컨** (pelican)
pelican
8) **홍학** (flamingo)
hong-hak
9) **비둘기** (pigeon)
bi-dul-gi
10) **올빼미** (owl)
ol-ppae-mi
11) **독수리** (vulture)
dok-su-ri
12) **독수리** (eagle)
dok-su-ri
13) **갈매기** (seagull)
gal-mae-gi
14) **까마귀** (crow)
kka-ma-gwi
15) **큰부리새** (toucan)
keun-bu-ri-sae
16) **펭귄** (penguin)
penguin
17) **딱따구리** (woodpecker)
ttak-tta-gu-ri
18) **마코앵무새** (macaw)
macaw aeng-mu-sae
19) **벌새** (hummingbird)
beol-sae
20) **키위새** (kiwi)
kiwi sae

호랑이는 한국의 상징이다.
The tiger is the symbol of Korea.

갈매기 떼가 배를 따라가고 있다.
A flock of seagulls is following the boat.

한국에서는 까마귀가 흉조라고 생각한다.
Crows are said to bring bad luck in Korea.

19
1
8
6
3
16
2
4
7
15
5
10
13
12
11
20
14
18
17
9

QUIZ #1

Use arrows to match the corresponding translations:

a. goldfish	1. 슬프다
b. leg	2. 손자
c. brother	3. 코
d. serious	4. 뇌
e. flamingo	5. 친절
f. mouse	6. 치타
g. cheetah	7. 호기심이 많다
h. neighbor	8. 고양이
i. cat	9. 홍학
j. sad	10. 오빠
k. kindness	11. 다리
l. grandson	12. 쥐
m. girlfriend	13. 금붕어
n. curious	14. 이웃
o. brain	15. 진지하다
p. nose	16. 여자친구

Fill in the blank spaces with the options below (use each word only once):

나의 오늘 하루는 정말 바쁠 것 같다. 오전에 할아버지와 _____를 뵙기로 했기 때문에 일찍부터 준비했다. 난 사랑하고 ____하는 조부모님을 오랜만에 뵙게 되어 너무나 ______. 할아버지께서 몇 년 전에 _____ 수술을 받으셨기 때문에 함께 모시고 병원에 갈 것이다.

검사가 끝나면 두 분을 모시고 동물원에 가보려고 한다. 우리 집 근처 동물원에는 코끼리, 사자, 하마 같은 동물들이 있는데, 특히 할머니는 _____를 좋아하신다. 할아버지는 새를 좋아하시는데, 그 중에서도 _____를 좋아하신다. 저녁에는 두 분께 내 _______를 소개시켜 드릴 것이다. 그는 얼굴도 잘 생겼지만 무엇보다도 착하고 _____하기 때문에 두 분이 마음에 들어 하실 것 같다. 맛있는 저녁 식사를 함께 하며 즐거운 시간을 보낼 것이다.

호랑이	남자친구
존경	친절
독수리	심장
기쁘다	할머니

파충류와 양서류 (REPTILES AND AMPHIBIANS)

- **파충류 (Reptiles)**
  pa-chung-nyu

1) **아나콘다** (anaconda)
   anaconda
2) **킹코브라** (king cobra)
   king cobra
3) **방울뱀** (rattlesnake)
   bang-ul-baem
4) **산호뱀** (coral snake)
   san-ho-baem
5) **뿔도마뱀** (horned lizard)
   ppul-do-ma-baem
6) **목도리도마뱀** (frill-necked lizard)
   mok-do-ri-do-ma-baem
7) **바실리스크도마뱀** (common basilisk/Jesus Christ lizard)
   basilisk do-ma-baem
8) **코모도왕도마뱀** (Komodo dragon)
   komodo-wang-do-ma-baem
9) **악어** (crocodile)
   a-geo
10) **인도 악어** (gharial/gavial)
    indo a-geo
11) **바다거북** (sea turtle)
    ba-da-geo-buk

- **양서류 (Amphibians)**
  yang-seo-ryu

12) **도룡뇽** (salamander)
    do-ryong-nyong
13) **골리앗개구리** (Goliath frog)
    goliath gae-gu-ri

이 강에는 악어가 득실거린다.
This river is full of crocodiles.

우린 진짜 살아 있는 방울뱀을 봤어!
We saw a real live rattlesnake!

환경 오염으로부터 바다거북을 보호해야만 한다.
We must protect sea turtles from pollution.

1
2
3
4
5
6
7
8
9
10
11
12
13

곤충과 거미류 (INSECTS AND ARACHNIDS)

- **곤충 (Insects)**
  gon-chung

1) **벌** (bee)
beol

2) **호박벌** (bumblebee)
ho-bak-beol

3) **말벌** (wasp)
mal-beol

4) **딱정벌레** (beetle)
ttak-jeong-beol-le

5) **나비** (butterfly)
na-bi

6) **나방** (moth)
na-bang

7) **잠자리** (dragonfly)
jam-ja-ri

8) **무당벌레** (ladybug)
mu-dang-beol-le

9) **반딧불이** (firefly)
ban-di-ppu-ri

10) **바퀴벌레** (cockroach)
ba-kwi-beol-le

11) **등에** (horsefly)
deung-e

12) **파리** (fly)
pa-ri

13) **모기** (mosquito)
mo-gi

14) **메뚜기** (grasshopper)
me-ttu-gi

15) **귀뚜라미** (cricket)
gwi-ttu-ra-mi

- **거미류 (Arachnids)**
  keo-mi-ryu

16) **전갈** (scorpion)
jeon-gal

17) **거미** (spider)
keo-mi

18) **흑색과부거미** (Southern black widow)
heuk-saek-gwa-bu-keo-mi

저는 거미를 엄청 싫어해요.
I really hate spiders.

나는 말벌에 쏘였다.
I got stung by a wasp.

가을에는 잠자리를 자주 볼 수 있다.
We can often see dragonflies in autumn.

12
11
2
15
1
14
13
9
18
6
7
16
5
3
10
4
8
17

포유류 I (MAMMALS I)

1) **박쥐** (bat)
   bak-jwi

2) **오리너구리** (platypus)
   o-ri-neo-gu-ri

3) **범고래** (killer whale/orca)
   beom-go-rae

4) **돌고래** (dolphin)
   dol-go-rae

5) **비버** (beaver)
   beaver

6) **마멋** (groundhog, marmot)
   ma-meot

7) **두더지** (mole)
   du-deo-ji

8) **다람쥐** (squirrel)
   da-ram-jwi

9) **족제비** (weasel)
   jok-je-bi

10) **주머니쥐** (possum/opossum)
    ju-meo-ni-jwi

11) **쥐** (rat)
    jwi

12) **토끼** (hare)
    to-kki

13) **오소리** (badger)
    o-so-ri

14) **스컹크** (skunk)
    skunk

15) **표범** (leopard)
    pyo-beom

바다에서 돌고래랑 수영해 본 적 있어?
Have you ever swum with dolphins in the ocean?

다람쥐 한 마리가 구멍 안으로 사라졌어.
A squirrel disappeared into a hole.

봐 봐, 그녀의 어깨 위에 쥐가 한 마리 있어!
Look, she has a rat on her shoulder!

9
1
10
8
14
7
11
5
15
2
6
13
3
12
4

포유류 II (MAMMALS II)

1) **곰** (bear)
   gom
2) **하이에나** (hyena)
   hyena
3) **자칼** (jackal)
   jackal
4) **소** (cow)
   so
5) **황소** (bull)
   hwang-so
6) **여우** (fox)
   yeo-u
7) **버팔로** (buffalo)
   buffalo
8) **고라니** (elk/moose)
   ko-ra-ni
9) **양** (sheep)
   yang
10) **염소** (goat)
    yeom-so
11) **가젤** (gazelle)
    gazelle
12) **늑대** (wolf)
    neuk-dae
13) **원숭이** (monkey)
    won-sung-i
14) **숫양** (ram)
    sun-nyang
15) **당나귀** (donkey)
    dang-na-gwi

저 나무에 원숭이 한 마리가 있다.
There is a monkey in the tree.

한국의 숲에서는 곰을 거의 볼 수 없다.
Bears can rarely be seen in the forests in Korea.

우리 할아버지께서는 시골에서 소를 많이 키우신다.
My grandfather raises many cows in the countryside.

12
13
1
14
5
4
15
10
11
7
9
8
6
3
2

물고기와 연체동물 (FISH AND MOLLUSKS)

- **물고기 (Fish)**
  mul-gogi

1) **고래상어** (whale shark)
   go-rae-sang-eo
2) **백상어** (white shark)
   baek-sang-eo
3) **귀상어** (hammerhead shark)
   gwi-sang-eo
4) **황새치 / 청새치** (swordfish/marlin)
   hwang-sae-chi / cheong-sae-chi
5) **창꼬치** (barracuda)
   chang-kko-chi
6) **복어** (pufferfish)
   bo-geo
7) **메기** (catfish)
   me-ki
8) **피라냐** (piranha)
   pi-ra-nya
9) **날치** (flying fish)
   nal-chi
10) **곰치** (moray eel)
    gom-chi
11) **쥐가오리** (manta ray)
    jwi-ga-o-ri
12) **해마** (seahorse)
    hae-ma

- **연체동물 (Mollusks)**
  yeon-che-dong-mul

13) **오징어** (squid)
    o-jing-eo
14) **갑오징어** (cuttlefish)
    ka-bo-jing-eo
15) **문어** (octopus)
    mu-neo
16) **굴** (oyster)
    kul
17) **조개** (clam)
    jo-gae
18) **앵무조개** (nautilus)
    aeng-mu-jo-gae
19) **달팽이** (snail)
    dal-paeng-i
20) **민달팽이** (slug)
    min-dal-paeng-i

메기는 일 년 내내 잡을 수 있습니다.
Catfish are in season all year round.

한국에서는 저렴한 가격에 신선한 굴을 맛볼 수 있습니다.
You can taste fresh oysters at a low price in Korea.

한국인들은 다양한 방법으로 오징어를 먹습니다.
Koreans enjoy eating squid in different ways.

20
19
16
18
15
17
14
7
1
6
5
13
11
10
9
12
2
8
3
4

의류 I (CLOTHING I)

1) **비옷** (raincoat)
bi-ot

2) **후드** (hoodie)
hood

3) **재킷** (jacket)
jacket

4) **청바지** (jeans)
cheong-ba-ji

5) **사각팬티** (boxer shorts)
sa-gak-paen-ti

6) **부츠** (boots)
boots

7) **귀걸이** (earrings)
gwi-geo-ri

8) **스웨터** (sweater)
sweater

9) **목걸이** (necklace)
mok-geo-ri

10) **브래지어** (bra)
beu-rae-ji-eo

11) **레깅스** (leggings)
leggings

12) **양말** (socks)
yang-mal

13) **블라우스 / 상의** (blouse/top)
blouse / sang-ui

14) **팔찌** (bracelet)
pal-jji

15) **반바지** (shorts)
ban-ba-ji

16) **팬티** (panties/underpants)
pantie

17) **코트** (coat)
coat

18) **원피스** (dress)
won-pi-seu

19) **지갑** (purse)
ji-gap

20) **샌들** (sandals)
sandal

난 원피스보다 청바지가 더 편해.
I feel more comfortable in jeans than in a dress.

내 양말에 구멍이 났네!
There is a hole in my sock!

추우면 스웨터를 입으렴.
If you are cold, wear a sweater.

1
3
6
9
7
8
2
4
10
5
12
20
14
11
13
16
17
18
15
19

의류 II (CLOTHING II)

1) **모자** (hat)
mo-ja

2) **턱시도** (tuxedo/smoking)
tuxedo

3) **나비넥타이** (bow tie)
na-bi *necktie*

4) **신발** (shoes)
shin-bal

5) **정장** (suit)
jeong-jang

6) **셔츠** (shirt)
shirts

7) **넥타이** (tie)
necktie

8) **서류 가방** (briefcase/case)
seo-ryu ga-bang

9) **긴 팔 블라우스** (long-sleeved blouse)
kin pal *blouse*

10) **스포츠 브라** (sports bra)
sports bra

11) **바지** (trousers/pants)
ba-ji

12) **벨트** (belt)
belt

13) **반지** (ring)
ban-ji

14) **티셔츠** (T-shirt)
T-shirts

15) **치마** (skirt)
chi-ma

16) **목도리** (scarf)
mok-do-ri

17) **시계** (watch)
shi-gye

18) **카고 바지** (cargo pants)
cargo ba-ji

19) **지갑** (wallet)
ji-gap

20) **우산** (umbrella)
u-san

어떡하죠, 저 지갑을 놓고 왔어요.
Oh no, I left my wallet behind.

새로 산 정장을 입으니까 너 정말 멋져 보인다!
You look really good in your new suit!

나는 비가 올 때를 대비해서 항상 우산을 갖고 다닌다.
I always have an umbrella with me in case it rains.

1
4
5
3
2
7
14
17
8
9
10
15
18
11
6
19
12
20
16
13

날씨 (THE WEATHER)

1) **화창하다** (sunny)
   hwa-chang-ha-da
2) **덥다** (hot)
   deop-da
3) **모래 폭풍** (sandstorm)
   mo-rae pok-pung
4) **흐리다** (cloudy)
   heu-ri-da
5) **따뜻하다** (warm)
   tta-tteu-ta-da
6) **안개가 끼다** (foggy/misty)
   an-gae-ga kki-da
7) **비가 오다** (rainy)
   bi-ga o-da
8) **시원하다** (cool)
   shi-won-ha-da
9) **빗방울** (raindrop)
   bit-bang-ul
10) **습하다** (humid)
   seu-pa-da
11) **폭풍** (storm)
   pok-pung
12) **번개** (lightning)
   beon-gae
13) **바람이 불다** (windy)
   ba-ra-mi bul-da
14) **눈이 오다** (snowy)
   nu-ni o-da
15) **춥다** (cold)
   chup-da
16) **눈송이** (snowflake)
   nun-song-i

한국은 1 월에 정말 추워요.
It is very cold in January in Korea.

하루 종일 비가 왔어요.
It's been rainy all day long.

오늘 날씨가 아주 화창해서 기분이 좋아요.
I feel good since it is so sunny today.

1
2
3

4
5
6

7
8
9
10

11
12
13

14
15
16

계절 – 봄 (THE SEASONS – SPRING)

1) **정원** (garden)
jeong-won

2) **꽃이 피다** (blossom)
kko-chi pi-da

3) **소풍** (picnic)
so-pung

4) **공원** (park)
gong-won

5) **자전거 타기** (bike ride)
ja-jeon-geo ta-gi

6) **레모네이드** (lemonade)
lemonade

7) **중고물건 판매** (garage sale)
jung-go-mul-geon pan-mae

8) **자동차 여행** (road trip)
ja-dong-cha yeo-haeng

9) **락페인팅을 하다** (to paint rocks)
rock painting-eul ha-da

10) **꽃을 심다** (to plant some flowers)
kko-cheul shim-tta

11) **연을 날리다** (to fly a kite)
yeo-neul nal-li-da

12) **바비큐 파티에 참석하다** (to attend a barbecue)
barbecue party-e cham-seo-ka-da

토요일에 공원에 산책하러 가요.
Let's go for a walk in the park on Saturday.

저희는 정원에 꽃을 심을 거예요.
We are going to plant some flowers in the garden.

우리는 한강을 따라 자전거 타는 걸 좋아해요.
We love bike rides along the Han River.

GARAGE SALE
LEMONADE
LEMO
WELCOME TO THE PARK
1
2
3
4
5
6
7
8
9
10
11
12

계절 – 여름 (THE SEASONS – SUMMER)

1) **캠핑을 가다** (to go camping)
   camping-eul ga-da
2) **워터파크** (water park)
   water park
3) **야외 활동** (outdoor activities)
   ya-oe hwal-ttong
4) **수영장** (swimming pool)
   su-yeong-jang
5) **수영하다** (to swim)
   su-yeong-ha-da
6) **선탠을 하다** (to get tanned)
   suntan-eul ha-da
7) **선크림** (sunscreen)
   suncream
8) **방충제** (insect repellent)
   bang-chung-je
9) **호수** (lake)
   ho-su
10) **인명 구조원** (lifesaver/lifeguard)
    in-myeong ku-jo-won
11) **모래성** (sandcastle)
    mo-rae-seong
12) **하이킹을 가다** (to go on a hike)
    hiking-eul ga-da

그녀는 수영을 잘 해.
She can swim well.

난 해변에서 선탠을 하는 걸 진짜 좋아해.
I love to tan on the beach.

네 선크림 잊지 마!
Do not forget your sunscreen!

9
12
3
1
8
2
11
7
4
5
6
10

QUIZ #2

Use arrows to match the corresponding translations:

a. horsefly	1. 화창하다
b. mole	2. 양말
c. king cobra	3. 반지
d. coat	4. 딱정벌레
e. socks	5. 두더지
f. Komodo dragon	6. 박쥐
g. tie	7. 따뜻하다
h. slug	8. 킹코브라
i. ring	9. 코트
j. snail	10. 등에
k. sunny	11. 목걸이
l. beetle	12. 달팽이
m. bat	13. 코모도왕도마뱀
n. warm	14. 나비
o. necklace	15. 넥타이
p. butterfly	16. 민달팽이

Fill in the blank spaces with the options below (use each word only once):

유민 씨는 오늘 걱정이 많습니다. 친구와 _____에서 만나기로 했는데 날씨가 좋지 않기 때문입니다. 일기예보에는 분명히 오늘 날씨가 ___________고 했는데 갑자기 비가 내리기 시작해서 그칠 기미가 보이지 않습니다. 그래서인지 3 월인데도 따뜻하지 않고, 오히려 ____고 느껴집니다.

원래 유민 씨는 ______에 티셔츠를 입고 나가려고 했는데, 비가 오기 때문에 ____을 입어야 하는지 고민 중입니다. 날씨가 좋았다면 한강 공원에서 __________도 할 수 있을 텐데 무척 아쉽습니다.

유민 씨는 추운 날씨를 엄청 싫어해서 빨리 여름이 오기를 바라고 있습니다. 여름이 되면 워터파크나 ______에도 갈 수 있고 캠핑도 할 수 있기 때문입니다. 다양한 __________을 할 수 있어서 유민 씨는 여름을 정말 좋아합니다.

자전거 타기

화창하다

비옷

수영장

야외 활동

공원

춥다

청바지

계절 - 가을 (THE SEASONS – FALL/AUTUMN)

1) **단풍** (changing leaves)
   dan-pung
2) **잎을 모으다** (to collect leaves)
   i-peul mo-eu-da
3) **호박** (pumpkin)
   ho-bak
4) **호박을 조각하다** (to carve a pumpkin)
   ho-ba-geul jo-ga-ka-da
5) **사과 따기** (apple picking)
   sa-gwa tta-gi
6) **할로윈 복장** (Halloween costume)
   Halloween bok-jang
7) **할로윈 사탕** (Halloween candy)
   Halloween sa-tang
8) **향초** (spiced candles)
   hyang-cho
9) **추수감사절 식사** (Thanksgiving dinner)
   chu-su-gam-sa-jeol shik-sa
10) **모직 담요** (wool blanket)
    mo-jik dam-nyo
11) **마시멜로를 굽다** (to roast marshmallows)
    marshmallow-reul gup-da
12) **뜰을 장식하다** (to decorate the yard)
    tteu-reul jang-shi-ka-da

10 월 말이면 한국 어디서나 아름다운 단풍을 볼 수 있습니다.
In late October, you can see the beautiful colors of changing leaves everywhere in Korea.

우리 엄마는 잎을 모아서 책갈피에 끼워 두신다.
My mom collects leaves and puts them between the pages of a book.

할머니 댁에 가서 사과를 따자.
Let's go to grandma's house to pick apples.

9
10
2
1
11
5
8
3
12
4
6
7

계절 - 겨울 (THE SEASONS – WINTER)

1) **핫초코** (hot cocoa/hot chocolate)
hot choco

2) **썰매** (sled)
sseol-mae

3) **벙어리장갑** (mittens)
beong-eo-ri-jang-gap

4) **패딩** (puffy jacket)
padding

5) **수프** (soup)
soup

6) **생강 쿠키** (gingerbread cookies)
saeng-gang *cookie*

7) **성에가 낀 창문** (frosty window)
seong-e-ga kkin chang-mun

8) **솔방울** (pinecone)
sol-ppang-ul

9) **아이스 스케이팅** (ice skating)
ice skating

10) **스키** (ski)
ski

11) **아이스 링크** (ice rink)
ice rink

12) **눈덩이** (snowball)
nun-tteong-i

난 불 옆에서 핫초코 마시는 게 진짜 좋아.
I love to drink hot chocolate near the fire.

저는 네 살 때 스키를 타기 시작했어요.
I started skiing at the age of 4.

수프가 준비됐습니다.
The soup is ready.

11
8
9
10
7
2
4
1
6
5
12
3

시간 (TIME)

1) **시간대** (time zone)
shi-gan-ttae

2) **초** (second)
cho

3) **분** (minute)
bun

4) **시, 시간** (hour)
shi, shi-gan

5) **날, 일** (day)
nal, il

6) **주** (week)
ju

7) **이(2) 주** (fortnight)
i ju

8) **달, 월** (month)
dal, wol

9) **해, 년** (year)
hae, nyeon

10) **새벽** (dawn)
sae-byeok

11) **아침** (morning)
a-chim

12) **정오** (noon/midday)
jeong-o

13) **오후** (afternoon)
o-hu

14) **해 질 녘** (dusk)
hae jil nyeok

15) **밤** (night)
bam

16) **자정** (midnight)
ja-jeong

17) **날짜** (date)
nal-jja

18) **달력** (calendar)
dal-lyeok

우리 딸은 아침 일찍 일어난다.
My daughter wakes up early in the morning.

결혼 기념일이 언제예요?
When is your wedding anniversary?

우리는 주로 정오에 점심을 먹는다.
We usually have lunch at noon.

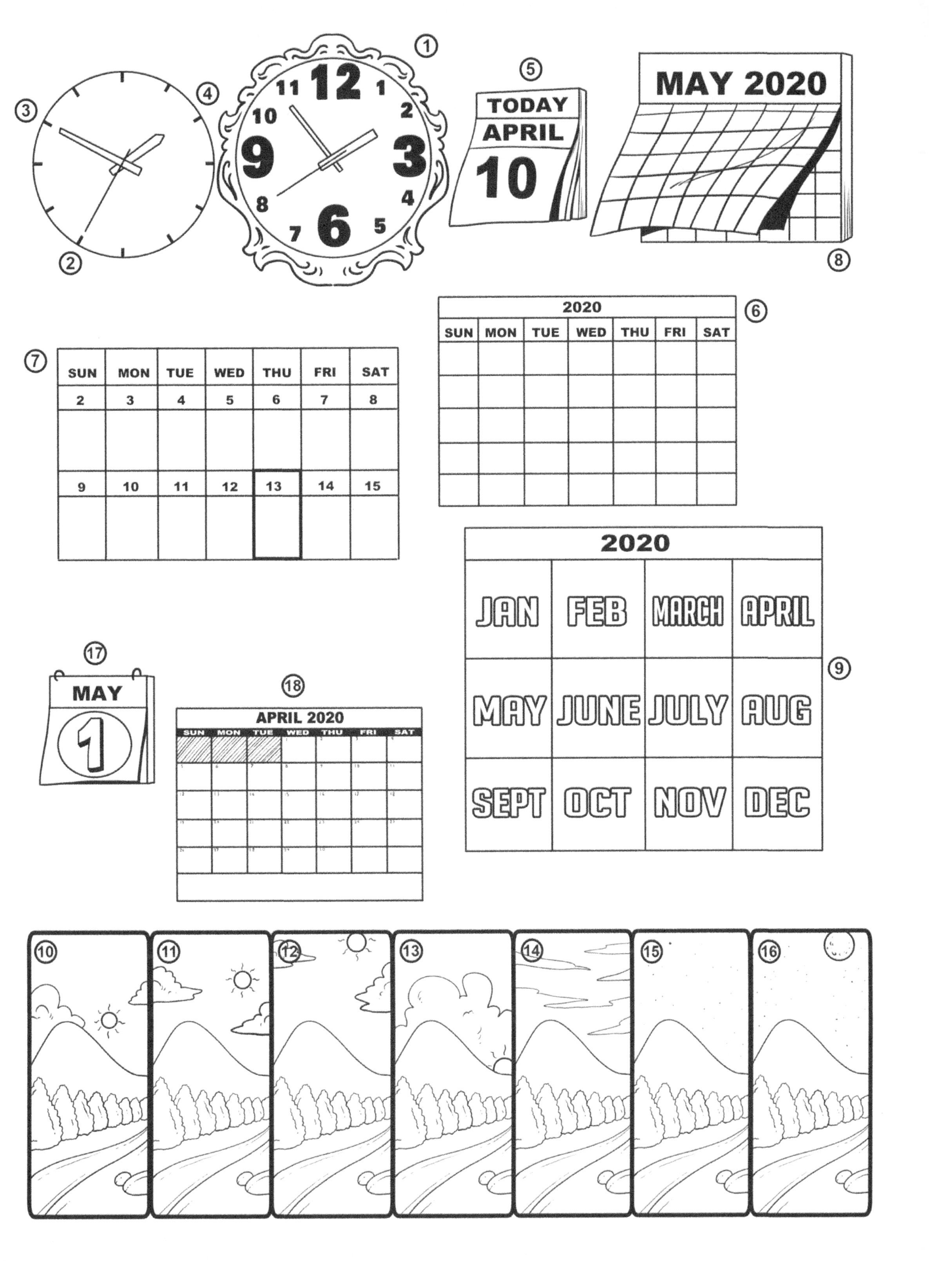

1
2
3
4
12
1
2
3
4
5
6
7
8
9
10
11
5
TODAY
APRIL
10
MAY 2020
8
2020
6
SUN MON TUE WED THU FRI SAT
7
SUN MON TUE WED THU FRI SAT
2 3 4 5 6 7 8
9 10 11 12 13 14 15
2020
JAN FEB MARCH APRIL
MAY JUNE JULY AUG
SEPT OCT NOV DEC
9
17
MAY
1
18
APRIL 2020
SUN MON TUE WED THU FRI SAT
10
11
12
13
14
15
16

집 (THE HOUSE)

1) **다락** (attic)
da-rak

2) **지붕** (roof)
ji-bung

3) **천장** (ceiling)
cheon-jang

4) **굴뚝** (chimney)
gul-ttuk

5) **벽** (wall)
byeok

6) **발코니** (balcony)
balcony

7) **현관** (porch)
hyeon-gwan

8) **창문** (window)
chang-mun

9) **셔터** (shutters)
shutter

10) **문** (door)
mun

11) **계단** (stairs)
gye-dan

12) **난간** (banister)
nan-gan

13) **바닥** (floor)
ba-dak

14) **지하실** (basement)
ji-ha-shil

15) **뒷마당** (backyard)
dwin-ma-dang

16) **차고** (garage)
cha-go

17) **진입로** (driveway)
ji-nip-no

18) **울타리** (fence/picket fence)
ul-ta-ri

19) **우편함** (mailbox)
u-pyeon-ham

20) **복도** (hallway/corridor)
bok-do

현관에 택배가 많이 와 있다.
There are lots of packages on the porch.

너네 집 뒷마당은 정말 아름답다.
Your backyard is very beautiful.

나 계단에서 넘어졌어.
I fell down the stairs.

1
2
3
4
5
6
7
8
9
10
11
12
13
14
15
16
17
18
19
20

주방 용품 (KITCHEN ITEMS)

1) **난로** (stove)
nal-lo
2) **전자레인지** (microwave oven)
jeon-ja-*range*
3) **오븐 토스터** (toaster oven)
oven toaster
4) **전기 믹서** (electric mixer)
jeon-gi *mixer*
5) **믹서기** (blender)
mixer-gi
6) **토스터기** (toaster)
toaster-gi
7) **커피 메이커** (coffee maker)
coffee maker
8) **냉장고** (fridge)
naeng-jang-go
9) **식품 저장고** (pantry)
shik-pum jeo-jang-go
10) **찬장** (cupboard)
chan-jang
11) **케이크 팬** (cake pan)
cake pan
12) **프라이팬** (frying pan)
peu-ra-i-*pan*
13) **냄비** (pot)
name-bi
14) **쿠키 커터** (cookie cutters)
cookie cutter
15) **믹싱 볼** (mixing bowl)
mixing bowl
16) **체** (colander)
che
17) **여과기** (strainer)
yeo-gwa-gi
18) **밀대** (rolling pin)
mil-ttae
19) **오븐용 장갑** (oven mitt)
oven-yong jang-gap
20) **앞치마** (apron)
ap-chi-ma

저는 믹서기를 사용해서 스무디를 만들었어요.
I used a blender to make a smoothie.

가서 냉장고에 있는 요거트 좀 가져와.
Go get a yogurt in the fridge.

난 밀대로 반죽을 밀었다.
I rolled the pastry with a rolling pin.

8
2
3
9
10
1
4
13
11
19
18
15
17
16
5
12
20
6
14
7

침실 용품 (BEDROOM ITEMS)

1) **침대** (bed)
chim-dae

2) **매트리스** (mattress)
mattress

3) **침구** (bedding/bed linen)
chim-gu

4) **베개** (pillow)
be-gae

5) **시트** (sheets)
sheet

6) **담요** (blanket)
dam-nyo

7) **침대보** (spread)
chim-dae-ppo

8) **베갯잇** (pillowcase)
be-gaen-nit

9) **침실용 스탠드** (nightstand)
chim-shil-lyong *stand*

10) **탁상 시계** (table clock)
tak-sang shi-gye

11) **탁상 조명** (table light)
tak-sang jo-myeong

12) **옷장** (closet)
ot-jjang

13) **흔들의자** (rocking chair)
heun-deu-lui-ja

14) **등** (lamp)
deung

15) **거울** (mirror)
keo-ul

16) **서랍장** (dresser)
seo-rap-jjang

17) **커튼** (curtain)
curtain

18) **요람** (cradle/crib)
yo-ram

19) **모빌** (crib mobile)
mobile

20) **옷걸이** (hanger)
ot-kkeo-ri

나는 침대보를 바꿀 거야.
I am going to change the bedsheets.

옷장 옆에 큰 거울이 있어요.
There is a big mirror next to the closet.

이 매트리스는 나한테 너무 딱딱해.
This mattress is too hard for me.

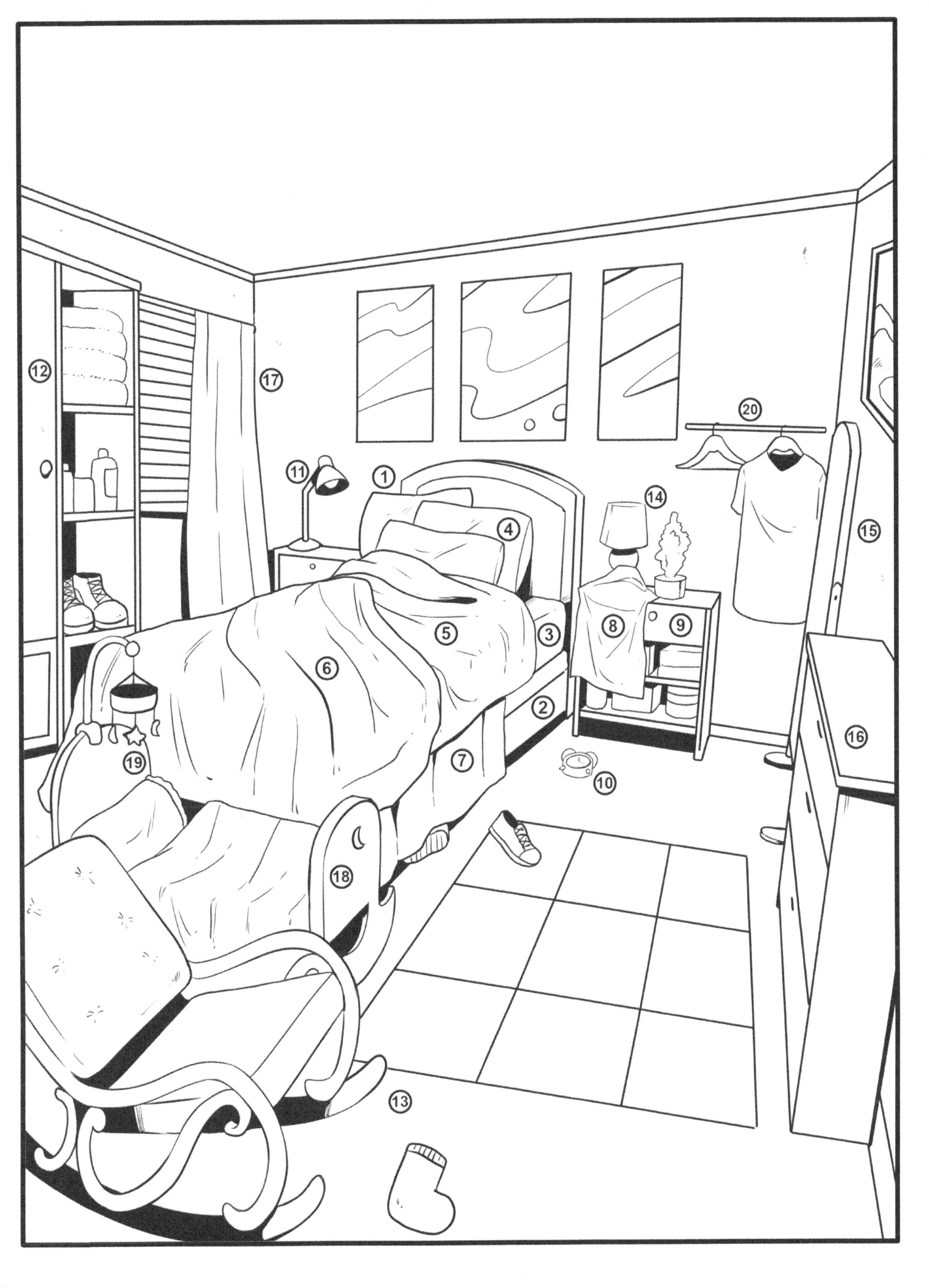

12
17
20
11
1
14
4
15
5
3
8
9
6
2
16
19
7
10
18
13

욕실 용품 (BATHROOM ITEMS)

1) **샤워 커튼** (shower curtain)
   shower curtain
2) **수건** (towel)
   su-geon
3) **수건걸이** (towel rack)
   su-geon-geo-ri
4) **핸드 타월** (hand towel)
   hand towel
5) **욕조** (bathtub)
   yok-jo
6) **샤워** (shower)
   shower
7) **화장실** (toilet/WC)
   hwa-jang-shil
8) **세면대** (sink/washbasin)
   se-myeon-dae
9) **수도꼭지** (faucet/tap)
   su-do-kkok-ji
10) **욕실 매트** (bathmat)
   yok-shil *mat*
11) **약품 수납장** (medicine cabinet)
   yak-pum su-nap-jang
12) **치약** (toothpaste)
   chi-yak
13) **칫솔** (toothbrush)
   chit-sol
14) **샴푸** (shampoo)
   shampoo
15) **빗** (comb)
   bit
16) **비누** (soap)
   bi-nu
17) **면도용 거품** (shaving foam)
   myeon-do-yong geo-pum
18) **면도기** (razor/shaver)
   myeon-do-gi
19) **화장지** (toilet paper)
   hwa-jang-ji
20) **배관 청소봉** (plunger)
   bae-gwan cheong-so-bong
21) **변기용 솔** (toilet brush)
   byeon-gi-yong sol
22) **휴지통** (wastebasket)
   hyu-ji-tong

치약과 칫솔은 세면대 위에 있습니다.
You can find a toothpaste and a toothbrush on the washbasin.

다 쓴 화장지는 휴지통에 넣으세요.
Put the used toilet paper into the wastebasket.

수도꼭지 잠그는 걸 잊지 마세요.
Do not forget to turn off the tap.

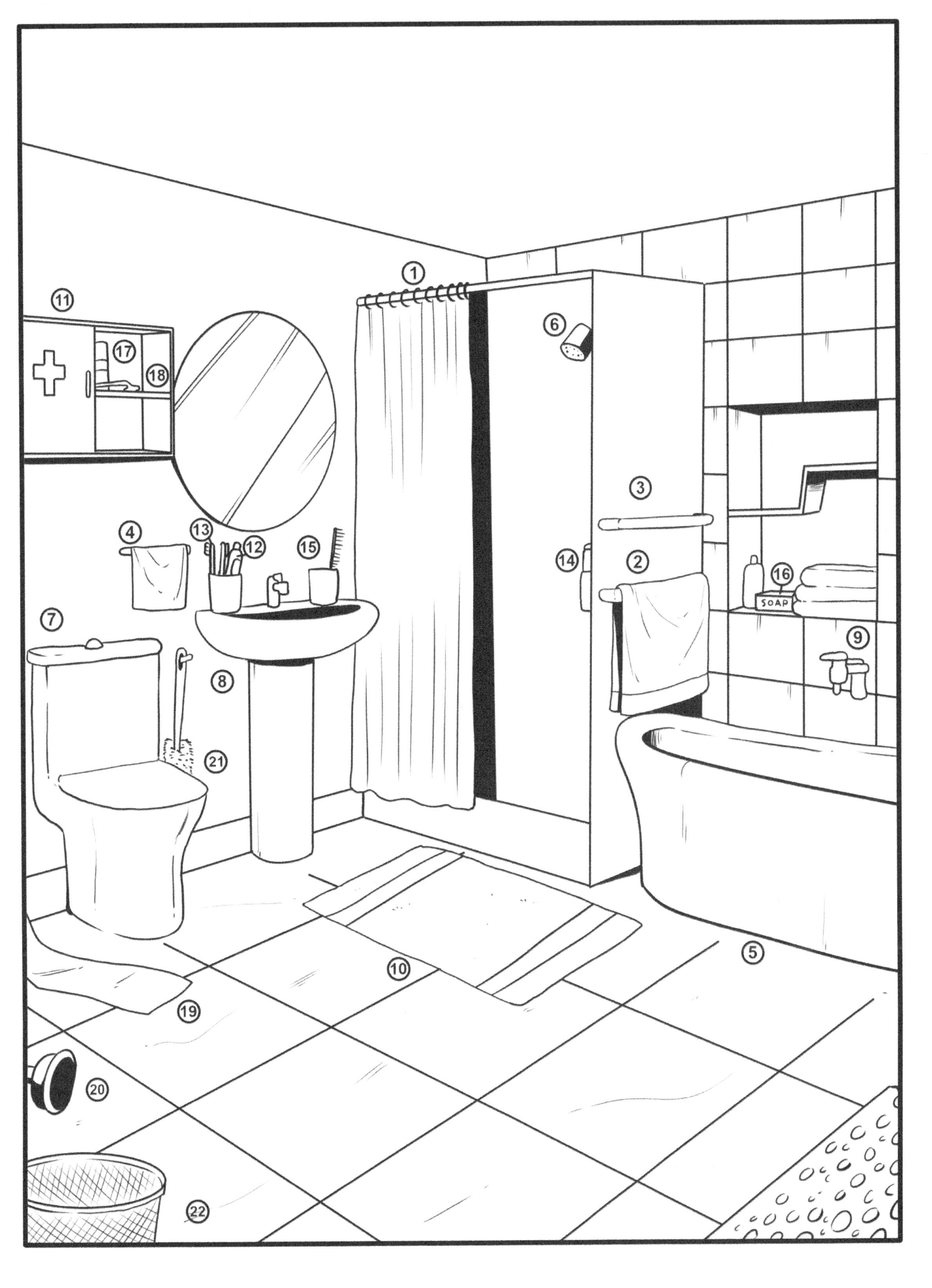
1
2
3
4
5
6
7
8
9
10
11
12
13
14
15
16
SOAP
17
18
19
20
21
22

거실 용품 (LIVING ROOM ITEMS)

1) **가구** (furniture)
ka-gu
2) **의자** (chair)
ui-ja
3) **소파** (sofa)
sofa
4) **소파** (couch)
sofa
5) **쿠션** (cushion)
cushion
6) **커피 테이블** (coffee table)
coffee table
7) **재떨이** (ashtray)
jae-tteo-ri
8) **꽃병** (vase)
kkot-byeong
9) **장식품** (ornaments)
jang-shik-pum
10) **책꽂이** (bookshelf/bookcase)
chaek-kko-ji
11) **잡지꽂이** (magazine holder)
jap-ji-kko-ji
12) **스테레오** (stereo)
stereo
13) **스피커** (speaker)
speaker
14) **벽난로** (fireplace)
byeong-nal-lo
15) **샹들리에** (chandelier)
shang-deul-li-e
16) **등** (lamp)
deung
17) **전구** (light bulb)
jeon-gu
18) **벽시계** (wall clock)
byeok-shi-gye
19) **그림** (painting)
geu-rim
20) **티브이 / 텔레비전** (TV/television)
TV / television
21) **리모컨** (remote control)
ri-mo-keon
22) **비디오게임기** (video game console)
video game-gi

난 티브이 앞에서 너무 시간을 많이 보낸다.
I spend too much time in front of the TV.

소파 위에 쿠션이 많이 있다.
There are many cushions on the sofa.

텔레비전 리모컨은 어디 있는 거야?
Where is the remote control of the television?

15
17
18
9
19
10
20
16
11
8
12
5
14
13
3
21
4
7
22
6
1
2

다이닝룸 용품 (DINING ROOM ITEMS)

1) **식탁** (dining table)
   shik-tak
2) **식탁보** (tablecloth)
   shik-tak-bo
3) **센터피스** (centerpiece)
   centerpiece
4) **식탁 매트** (placemat)
   shik-tak *mat*
5) **접시** (plate)
   jeop-shi
6) **냅킨** (napkin)
   napkin
7) **칼, 나이프** (knife)
   kal, *knife*
8) **포크** (fork)
   fork
9) **숟가락, 스푼** (spoon)
   sut-ka-rak, *spoon*
10) **병** (pitcher/jar)
    byeong
11) **유리컵** (glass)
    yu-ri-*cup*
12) **컵** (mug/cup)
    cup
13) **소금통** (saltshaker)
    so-geum-tong
14) **후추통** (pepper shaker)
    hu-chu-tong
15) **쟁반** (tray)
    jaeng-ban
16) **음료수** (drink/beverage)
    eum-nyo-su
17) **음식** (food)
    eum-shik
18) **간식** (snack)
    kan-shik

숟가락이 한 개 더 필요해요.
I need one more spoon.

소금통 좀 건네 주시겠어요?
Could you pass me the saltshaker?

식탁 위에 물병이 하나 있다.
There is a water pitcher on the dining table.

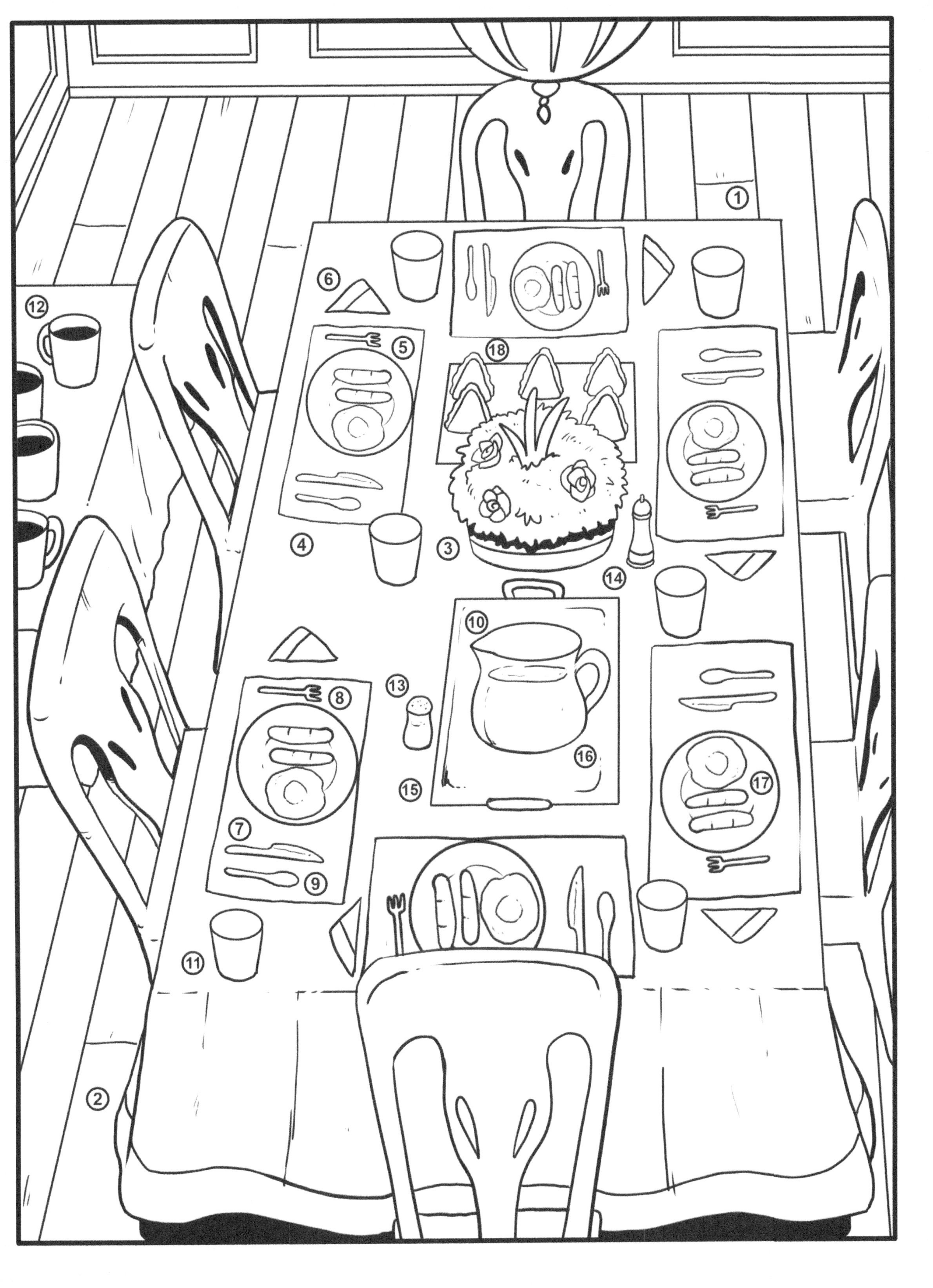
1
6
12
5
18
4
3
14
10
13
8
16
15
17
7
9
11
2

QUIZ #3

Use arrows to match the corresponding translations:

a. morning	1. 창문
b. pumpkin	2. 옷장
c. door	3. 썰매
d. Halloween costume	4. 벽
e. pillow	5. 앞치마
f. afternoon	6. 눈덩이
g. sled	7. 베개
h. apron	8. 할로윈 복장
i. ice rink	9. 문
j. towel rack	10. 토스터기
k. wall	11. 오후
l. closet	12. 수건걸이
m. window	13. 아이스 링크
n. fireplace	14. 호박
o. snowball	15. 벽난로
p. toaster	16. 아침

Fill in the blank spaces with the options below (use each word only once):

우리 가족은 오늘 집안 대청소를 했어요. 추석 명절이 바로 다음 _____에 시작하기 때문이죠. 이모와 이모부, 그리고 사촌 동생들과 삼촌네 가족이 오시기 때문에 침대를 정리하고 베개와 ______를 여러 개 준비했어요. 욕실에는 샤워 후에 사용할 ____도 넉넉히 놓아 두었어요. 치약과 _____, 샴푸도 새 것으로 바꿔 놓았죠. 우리 엄마는 많은 식구가 먹을 _____도 냉장고 안에 넉넉히 사두셨어요. 그리고 ____와 숟가락도 많이 필요하죠. 나는 벌써부터 친척들이 우리 집에 올 때가 기대돼요. 우리는 같이 거실에 있는 에 앉아서 재미있게 얘기도 나누고 ____도 구경하러 갈 거예요.

수건

소파

단풍

주

접시

칫솔

담요

음식

정원 (THE GARDEN/THE BACKYARD)

1) **정원사** (gardener)
jeong-won-sa

2) **창고** (shed)
chang-ko

3) **덤불** (bush)
deom-bul

4) **잔디** (lawn)
jan-di

5) **풀** (grass)
pul

6) **꽃** (flower)
kkot

7) **정원용 호스** (garden hose)
jeong-won-nyong *hose*

8) **물뿌리개** (watering can)
mul-ppu-ri-gae

9) **화분** (flowerpot)
hwa-bun

10) **원예용 장갑** (gardening gloves)
wo-nye-yong jang-gap

11) **삽** (shovel)
sap

12) **갈퀴** (rake)
gal-kwi

13) **가드닝 포크** (gardening fork)
gardening fork

14) **전지 가위** (pruners/pruning shears)
jeon-ji ga-wi

15) **모종삽** (garden trowel)
mo-jong-sap

16) **수도꼭지** (tap)
su-do-kkok-ji

17) **손수레** (wheelbarrow)
son-su-re

18) **잔디 깎기 기계** (lawn mower)
jan-di kka-kki ki-gae

19) **손전등** (lantern)
son-jjeon-deung

20) **덩굴** (vine)
deong-gul

정원에 덩굴이 자라고 있다.
A vine grows in my garden.

창고에 도구를 전부 넣어 두었다.
I have put all my tools in the shed.

손수레가 낙엽으로 꽉 찼다.
The wheelbarrow is full of dead leaves.

2
3
19
5
6
18
16
11
4
1
9
7
13
17
20
12
8
10
14
15

세탁실 (THE CLEANING ROOM)

1) **세탁기** (washing machine)
se-tak-ki

2) **건조기** (dryer)
geon-jo-gi

3) **다리미** (iron)
da-ri-mi

4) **다리미 판** (ironing board)
da-ri-mi pan

5) **세탁 비누** (laundry soap)
se-tak bi-nu

6) **세제** (laundry detergent)
se-je

7) **섬유유연제** (fabric softener)
seo-myu-yu-yeon-je

8) **빨래 바구니** (laundry basket)
ppal-lae ba-gu-ni

9) **더러운 옷** (dirty clothes)
deo-reo-un ot

10) **깨끗한 세탁물** (clean laundry)
kkae-kkeu-tan se-tang-mul

11) **빗자루** (broom)
bit-ja-ru

12) **쓰레받기** (dust pan)
sseu-re-bat-gi

13) **고무장갑** (rubber gloves)
go-mu-jang-gap

14) **스펀지** (sponge)
sponge

15) **플라스틱 통** (plastic tub)
plastic tong

16) **대걸레** (mop)
dae-geol-le

17) **양동이** (bucket)
yang-dong-i

18) **세척용 헝겊** (cleaning cloths)
se-cheong-nyong heong-geop

19) **세탁솔** (scrub brush)
se-tak-sol

20) **표백제** (bleach)
pyo-baek-je

21) **살균제** (disinfectant)
sal-gyun-je

22) **쓰레기통** (garbage can)
sseu-re-gi-tong

난 빨래하는 게 엄청 싫어.
I hate doing the laundry.

여러분은 바닥을 대걸레로 닦아야 해요.
You must mop the floor.

세탁기에 섬유유연제를 사용할 수 있습니다.
You can use fabric softener in the washing machine.

1
2
3
4
5
6
7
8
9
10
11
12
13
14
15
16
17
18
19
20
21
22

학교 / 대학교 (THE SCHOOL/THE UNIVERSITY)

1) **선생님** (teacher)
   seon-saeng-nim
2) **학생** (student)
   hak-saeng
3) **교실** (classroom)
   kyo-shil
4) **사물함** (locker)
   sa-mul-ham
5) **게시판** (bulletin board)
   ke-shi-pan
6) **종이** (sheet of paper)
   jong-i
7) **책** (book)
   chaek
8) **공책** (notebook)
   kong-chaek
9) **풀** (glue)
   pul
10) **가위** (scissors)
   ga-wi
11) **연필** (pencil)
   yeon-pil
12) **지우개** (eraser)
   ji-u-gae
13) **연필깎이** (pencil sharpener)
   yeon-pil-kka-kki
14) **펜** (pen)
   pen
15) **마커** (marker)
   marker
16) **형광펜** (highlighter)
   hyeong-gwang-*pen*
17) **봉투** (envelope)
   bong-tu
18) **클립보드** (clipboard)
   clipboard
19) **칠판** (blackboard)
   chil-pan
20) **계산기** (calculator)
   gye-san-gi
21) **자** (ruler)
   ja
22) **스테이플러** (stapler)
   stapler
23) **필통** (pouch/pencil case)
   pil-tong
24) **학교 책상** (school desk)
   hak-kko chaek-sang
25) **교탁** (table)
   gyo-tak
26) **노트북 컴퓨터** (laptop)
   notebook computer

이 계산은 계산기 없이는 너무 복잡하다.
This calculation is too complicated without a calculator.

내 연필깎이를 찾을 수가 없어.
I cannot find my pencil sharpener.

CLASS-B
1
2
3
4
5
6
7
8
9
10
11
12
13
14
15
16
17
18
19
20
21
22
23
24
25
26

사무실 (THE OFFICE)

1) **상사** (boss)
sang-sa

2) **선배** (superior)
seon-bae

3) **직원** (employee)
ji-kwon

4) **대표** (CEO/president)
dae-pyo

5) **사업 파트너** (business partner)
sa-eop *partner*

6) **동료** (colleague)
dong-nyo

7) **동료** (co-worker)
dong-nyo

8) **비서** (secretary)
bi-seo

9) **칸막이 사무실** (cubicle)
kan-ma-gi sa-mu-shil

10) **회전의자** (swivel chair)
hoe-jeo-nui-ja

11) **책상** (desk)
chaek-sang

12) **컴퓨터** (computer)
computer

13) **프린터** (printer)
printer

14) **사무용품** (office supplies)
sa-mu-yong-pum

15) **고무도장** (rubber stamp)
go-mu-do-jang

16) **테이프 디스펜서** (tape dispenser)
tape dispenser

17) **폴더** (folder)
folder

18) **서류함** (filing cabinet)
seo-ryu-ham

19) **팩스** (fax)
fax

20) **전화기** (telephone)
jeon-hwa-gi

난 내 동료가 진짜 마음에 들어.
I really like my colleague.

당신의 번호는 제 비서에게 주세요.
Give your number to my secretary.

이제 아무도 팩스를 사용하지 않아요!
No one uses a fax anymore!

9
18
7
1
3
6
12
4
8
15
2
10
16
20
5
13
11
14
19
17

직업 (PROFESSIONS/OCCUPATIONS)

1) **엔지니어** (engineer)
engineer

2) **우주비행사** (astronaut)
u-ju-bi-haeng-sa

3) **조종사** (pilot)
jo-jong-sa

4) **판사** (judge)
pan-sa

5) **소방관** (firefighter)
so-bang-gwan

6) **경찰관** (police officer)
gyeong-chal-gwan

7) **요리사** (chef)
yo-ri-sa

8) **지휘자** (conductor)
ji-hwi-ja

9) **교수** (professor)
gyo-su

10) **댄서** (dancer)
dancer

11) **사업가** (businessman)
sa-eop-kka

12) **조련사** (animal trainer)
jo-ryeon-sa

저는 어렸을 때 조종사가 되고 싶었어요.
When I was a kid, I wanted to be a pilot.

그는 훌륭한 사업가가 될 것이다.
He will become a good businessman.

소방관을 불러!
Call the firefighters!

12
10
2
5
8
1
4
6
7
9
3
11

교통수단 (MEANS OF TRANSPORT)

1) **자전거** (bike/bicycle)
ja-jeon-geo

2) **오토바이** (motorcycle/motorbike)
o-to-ba-i

3) **스노모빌** (snowmobile)
snowmobile

4) **차, 자동차** (car/automobile)
cha, ja-dong-cha

5) **버스** (bus)
bus

6) **트럭** (truck)
truck

7) **지하철** (subway)
ji-ha-cheol

8) **기차** (train)
ki-cha

9) **제트스키** (jet ski)
jet ski

10) **배** (boat)
bae

11) **유람선** (cruise ship)
yu-ram-seon

12) **잠수함** (submarine)
jam-su-ham

13) **비행선** (blimp/Zeppelin)
bi-haeng-seon

14) **열기구** (hot-air balloon)
yeol-ki-gu

15) **비행기** (plane/airplane)
bi-haeng-gi

16) **헬리콥터** (helicopter/chopper)
helicopter

17) **우주 왕복선** (space shuttle)
u-ju wang-bok-sseon

버스 타고 갈 거야 아니면 차 타고 갈 거야?
Are you going to take the bus or your car?

나는 열기구를 타 본 적이 없다.
I have never gotten on a hot-air balloon.

서울에는 편리한 버스와 지하철 시스템이 있다.
Seoul has a very convenient system of buses and subways.

3
6
1
9
8
13
16
14
10
11
SUBWAY
7
4
17
15
5
12
SCHOOL BUS
2

풍경 (LANDSCAPES)

1) **산** (mountain)
   san
2) **열대우림** (tropical rainforest)
   yeol-ttae-u-rim
3) **사막** (desert)
   sa-mak
4) **화산** (volcano)
   hwa-san
5) **절벽** (cliff)
   jeol-byeok
6) **바닷가** (beach)
   ba-dat-kka
7) **숲** (forest)
   sup
8) **동굴** (cave)
   dong-gul
9) **온천** (geyser/hot spring)
   on-cheon
10) **폭포** (waterfall/falls)
    pok-po
11) **강** (river)
    gang
12) **고대 유적** (ancient ruins)
    go-dae-yu-jeok

나 숲 속에서 길을 잃었어.
I got lost in the forest.

많은 사람들이 여름을 즐기러 바닷가에 왔다.
A lot of people came to the beach to enjoy the summer.

우린 강을 건너야 한다.
We must cross the river.

5
7
1
8
11
9
10
2
4
6
12
3

운동 I (SPORTS I)

1) **양궁** (archery)
   yang-gung
2) **권투** (boxing)
   gwon-tu
3) **사이클링** (cycling)
   cycling
4) **펜싱** (fencing)
   fencing
5) **축구** (football/soccer)
   chuk-gu
6) **럭비** (rugby)
   rugby
7) **탁구** (table tennis/ping-pong)
   tak-gu
8) **배구** (volleyball)
   bae-gu
9) **역도** (weightlift)
   yeok-do
10) **스케이팅** (skating)
    skating
11) **패럴림픽 경기** (paralympic sports)
    paralympic gyeong-gi
12) **야구** (baseball)
    ya-gu
13) **농구** (basketball)
    nong-gu

한국 양궁 팀은 매우 강력하다.
The Korean archery teams are very strong.

한국 사람들은 축구와 야구를 즐긴다.
Korean people enjoy soccer and baseball.

우리 아들은 학교 끝난 후에 농구하는 걸 좋아한다.
My son likes to play basketball after school.

3
2
1
4
6
9
13
70
8
7
12
5
10
11

운동 II (SPORTS II)

1) **배드민턴** (badminton)
badminton

2) **체조** (gymnastics)
che-jo

3) **조정** (rowing)
jo-jeong

4) **스포츠 클라이밍** (sport climbing)
sports climbing

5) **서핑** (surfing)
surfing

6) **테니스** (tennis)
tennis

7) **트램펄린** (trampoline)
trampoline

8) **레슬링** (wrestling)
wrestling

9) **스키** (skiing)
ski

10) **스켈레톤** (skeleton)
skeleton

11) **피겨 스케이팅** (figure skating)
figure skating

12) **수영** (swimming)
su-yeong

13) **수구** (water polo)
su-gu

14) **하키** (hockey)
hockey

한국에서는 피겨 스케이팅의 인기가 점점 높아지고 있다.
Figure skating is becoming more and more popular in Korea.

라파엘 나달은 최고의 테니스 선수이다.
Rafael Nadal is the best tennis player.

수구는 한국에서는 잘 알려져 있지 않다.
Water polo is not very common in Korea.

8
5
4
3
13
1
12
7
2
11
14
9
10
6

크리스마스 (CHRISTMAS DAY)

1) **겨우살이** (mistletoe)
gyeo-u-sa-ri

2) **화환** (garland)
hwa-hwan

3) **크리스마스 트리** (Christmas tree)
Christmas tree

4) **크리스마스 장식** (Christmas decorations)
Christmas jang-shik

5) **크리스마스 선물** (Christmas gifts/presents)
Christmas seon-mul

6) **크리스마스 식사** (Christmas dinner)
Christmas shik-sa

7) **지팡이사탕** (candy cane)
ji-pang-i-sa-tang

8) **생강쿠키** (gingerbread man)
saeng-gang *cookie*

9) **크리스마스 요정** (Christmas elf)
Christmas yo-jeong

10) **크리스마스 모자** (Christmas hat)
Christmas mo-ja

11) **산타클로스, 산타** (Santa Claus)
Santa Claus, Santa

12) **산타 썰매** (Santa's sleigh)
Santa sseol-mae

13) **크리스마스 별** (Christmas star)
Christmas byeol

14) **눈사람** (snowman)
nun-ssa-ram

15) **양초** (candles)
yang-cho

우린 백화점에서 크리스마스 장식을 샀다.
We bought Christmas decorations at the department store.

내 사촌이랑 나는 어제 밤에 눈사람을 만들었어.
My cousin and I built a snowman last night.

크리스마스 선물로 뭐가 좋을까?
What would be good for Christmas gifts?

13
4
12
3
2
14
10
5
1
9
11
15
6
7
8

QUIZ #4

Use arrows to match the corresponding translations:

a. engineer	1. 소방관
b. printer	2. 계산기
c. wheelbarrow	3. 배
d. mop	4. 더러운 옷
e. colleague	5. 세탁기
f. gardener	6. 갈퀴
g. bike	7. 프린터
h. cave	8. 비행기
i. plane	9. 손수레
j. calculator	10. 정원사
k. firefighter	11. 동료
l. boat	12. 자전거
m. dirty clothes	13. 대걸레
n. washing machine	14. 동굴
o. rake	15. 엔지니어

Fill in the blank spaces with the options below (use each word only once):

오늘 저녁에는 회사 _______의 가족이 우리 집을 방문했다. 그의 아내는 학생들을 가르치고 있는데, 대한 고등학교의 영어 _________이다. 그 부부의 아들은 ______를 잘 해서 지금 축구 선수로 활동하고 있다. 날씨가 좋아서 우리는 정원에서 바비큐 파티를 했다. 정원에서 자라고 있는 나무와 ____을 보면서 정원 관리에 대한 얘기를 나누었다. 그리고 서로의 여행담도 주고 받았는데, 동료는 가족 여행으로 제주도에 갔던 얘기를 했다. 제주도의 멋진 절벽과 ____ 앞에서 찍은 사진을 보여주기도 했다. 특히 ______를 처음으로 타본 경험을 얘기했는데, 내게도 꼭 한 번 타보라며 추천했다. 우리 가족은 강원도의 ______에서 찍은 사진을 보여줬다. 다음에는 두 가족이 같이 ___에 올라가자고 약속했다.

꽃	동료
폭포	산
선생님	열기구
바닷가	축구

악기 (MUSICAL INSTRUMENTS)

1) **어쿠스틱 기타** (acoustic guitar)
acoustic guitar

2) **일렉트릭 기타** (electric guitar)
electric guitar

3) **베이스 기타** (bass guitar)
bass guitar

4) **드럼** (drums)
drum

5) **피아노** (piano)
piano

6) **트럼펫** (trumpet)
trumpet

7) **하모니카** (harmonica)
harmonica

8) **플루트** (flute)
flute

9) **클라리넷** (clarinet)
clarinet

10) **하프** (harp)
harp

11) **백파이프** (bagpipes)
bagpipe

12) **첼로** (cello)
cello

13) **바이올린** (violin)
violin

14) **색소폰** (saxophone)
saxophone

난 피아노 수업을 듣기 시작했어.
I have started taking piano lessons.

하프는 내가 가장 좋아하는 악기야.
The harp is my favorite instrument.

지미 헨드릭스는 기타의 천재였어.
Jimi Hendrix is a guitar genius.

1
3
6
8
11
7
10
2
12
5
9
14
4
13

과일 (FRUITS)

1) **딸기** (strawberry)
   ttal-gi
2) **파파야** (papaya)
   papaya
3) **자두** (plum)
   ja-du
4) **멜론** (melon)
   melon
5) **수박** (watermelon)
   su-bak
6) **바나나** (banana)
   banana
7) **망고** (mango)
   mango
8) **복숭아** (peach)
   bok-sung-a
9) **산딸기** (raspberry)
   san-ttal-gi
10) **오렌지** (orange)
    orange
11) **레몬** (lemon)
    lemon
12) **파인애플** (pineapple)
    pineapple
13) **라임** (lime)
    lime
14) **포도** (grapes)
    po-do
15) **체리** (cherry)
    cherry
16) **사과** (apple)
    sa-gwa
17) **배** (pear)
    bae
18) **자몽** (grapefruit)
    ja-mong
19) **구아바** (soursop)
    guava
20) **코코넛** (coconut)
    coconut

배 한 봉지 주세요.
I would like a bag of pears, please.

그는 아침 식사로 자몽 한 개를 먹는다.
He eats a grapefruit for breakfast.

난 산딸기 잼이 진짜 마음에 들어.
I love raspberry jam.

20
10
17
16
3
9
4
6
13
18
19
7
15
14
2
8
12
1
11
5

채소 (VEGETABLES)

1) **콜리플라워** (cauliflower)
   cauliflower
2) **아스파라거스** (asparagus)
   asparagus
3) **브로콜리** (broccoli)
   broccoli
4) **양배추** (cabbage)
   yang-bae-chu
5) **아티초크** (artichoke)
   artichoke
6) **방울양배추** (Brussels sprout)
   bang-ul-yang-bae-chu
7) **옥수수** (corn)
   ok-su-su
8) **상추** (lettuce)
   sang-chu
9) **시금치** (spinach)
   shi-geum-chi
10) **토마토** (tomato)
    to-ma-to
11) **오이** (cucumber)
    o-i
12) **애호박** (zucchini)
    ae-ho-bak
13) **버섯** (mushroom)
    beo-seot
14) **루콜라** (arugula)
    ru-kol-la
15) **가지** (eggplant)
    ga-ji
16) **피망** (bell pepper)
    pi-man
17) **양파** (onion)
    yang-pa
18) **호박** (pumpkin/squash)
    ho-bak
19) **감자** (potato)
    gam-ja
20) **근대** (Swiss chard)
    geun-dae

난 호박죽을 준비했어.
I prepared a pumpkin soup.

이 김밥에는 오이가 들어간다.
This gimbap has cucumbers in it.

한국 사람들은 돼지고기 구이를 상추와 함께 즐긴다.
Koreans enjoy pork barbecue with lettuce.

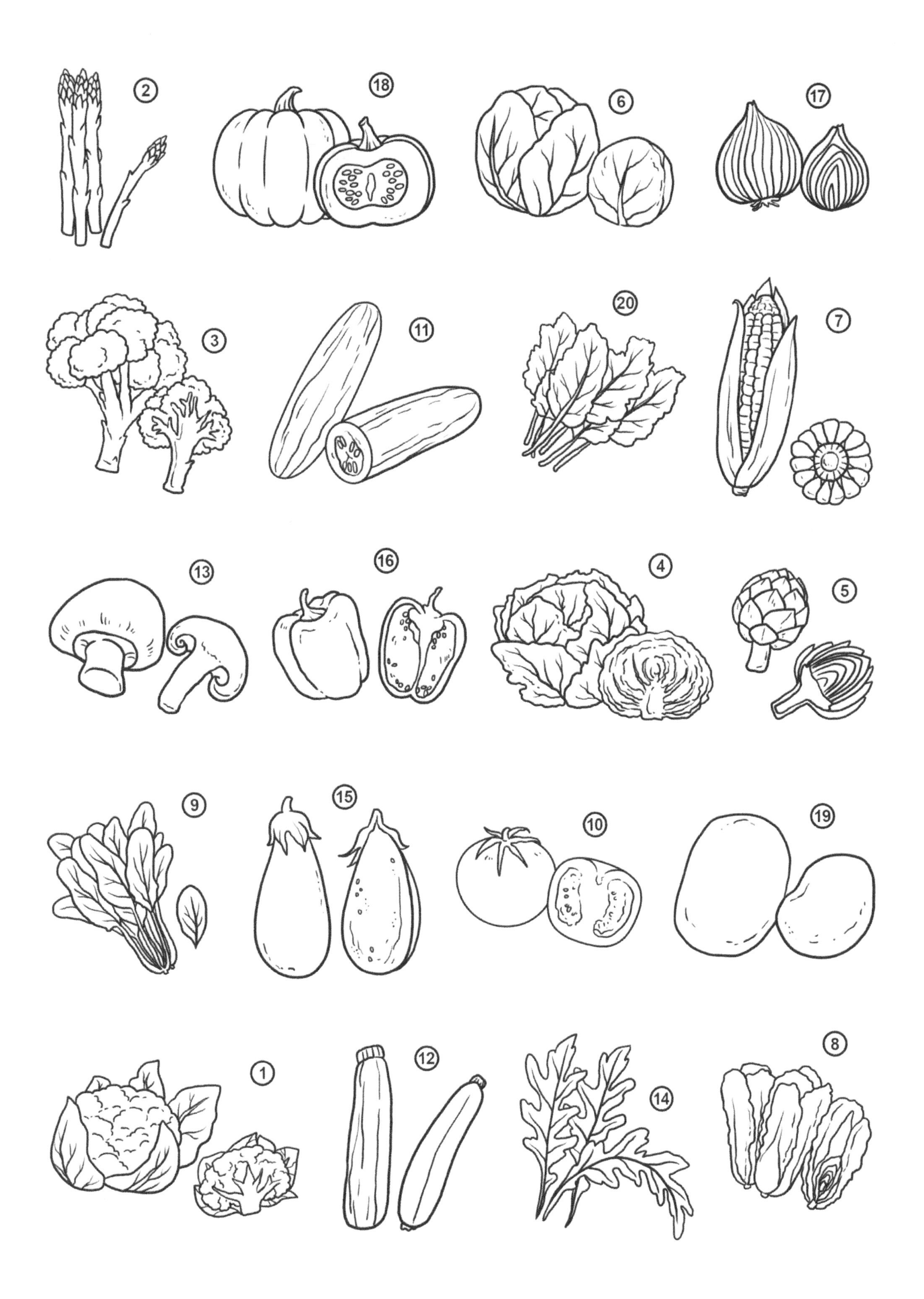

2
18
6
17
3
11
20
7
13
16
4
5
9
15
10
19
1
12
14
8

기술 (TECHNOLOGY)

1) **핸드폰** (mobile)
han-deu-pon
2) **기기** (device)
ki-gi
3) **컴퓨터** (computer)
computer
4) **웹캠** (web cam)
web cam
5) **USB 저장장치** (flash drive)
USB jeo-jang-jang-chi
6) **하드 드라이브** (hard drive)
hard drive
7) **메모리 카드** (memory card)
memory card
8) **카드 리더기** (card reader)
card reader-gi
9) **무선** (wireless)
mu-seon
10) **태양 전지판** (solar panel)
tae-yang-jeon-ji-pan
11) **프린터** (printer)
printer
12) **스캐너** (scanner)
scanner

나는 메모리 카드를 교체해야 한다.
I have to replace the memory card.

너네 프린터 사용해도 되니?
Can I use your printer?

저는 이 기기에 그 서류를 다운받았어요.
I have downloaded the document into this device.

1
2
3
4
5
6
7
8
9
10
11
12
2TB

과학 (SCIENCE)

1) **실험실** (laboratory)
   shil-heom-shil
2) **연구원** (researcher)
   yeon-gu-won
3) **계산** (calculations)
   gye-san
4) **과학자** (scientist)
   gwa-hak-ja
5) **실험실 가운** (lab coat)
   shil-heom-shil *gown*
6) **실험** (experiment)
   shil-heom
7) **개인 보호 장비** (personal protective equipment)
   gae-in bo-ho jang-bi
8) **테스트, 검사** (test)
   test, geom-sa
9) **상** (prize)
   sang
10) **위험** (risk)
    wi-heom
11) **기구** (instrument)
    ki-gu
12) **통계학** (statistics)
    tong-gye-hak

실험실에서는 개인 보호 장비가 필수적입니다.
Personal protective equipment is mandatory in the laboratory.

저는 코로나 검사 받으러 왔는데요.
I have come for a COVID-19 test.

그는 과학자이다.
He works as a scientist.

1
2
3
4
5
6
7
8
9
10
11
12
H-C-C-O-H
C_2H_5OH
$2x - 3^2 = 10x$
$Au(s) + 3NO_3^-(aq) + 6H^+(aq) \rightarrow Au^{3+}(aq) + 3NO_2$
$Au^{3+}(aq) + 4Cl^-$
$\rightarrow AuCl_4^-$
H_3C
N
CH_2
H_3C
$9_2 + 6_2 = ?$
2×1×1−0
50
40
30
20
10
1 2 3 4 5

천문학 (ASTRONOMY)

1) **망원경** (telescope)
mang-won-gyeong

2) **태양, 해** (sun)
tae-yang, hae

3) **달** (moon)
dal

4) **은하, 은하수** (galaxy, Milky Way)
eun-ha, eun-ha-su

5) **소행성대** (asteroid belt)
so-haeng-seong-dae

6) **블랙홀** (black hole)
black hole

7) **식** (eclipse)
shik

8) **유성, 별똥별** (shooting star)
yu-seong, byeol-ttong-byeol

9) **우주 정거장** (space station)
u-ju jeong-geo-jang

10) **백색 왜성** (white dwarf)
baek-saek wae-seong

11) **적색 거성** (red giant)
jeok-saek keo-seong

12) **궤도** (orbit)
gwe-do

13) **별자리** (constellation)
byeol-jja-ri

14) **암흑 에너지** (dark energy)
am-heuk *energy*

15) **명왕성** (Pluto)
myeong-wang-seong

16) **성운** (Nebula)
seong-un

17) **수성** (Mercury)
su-seong

18) **금성** (Venus)
geum-seong

19) **지구** (Earth)
ji-gu

20) **화성** (Mars)
hwa-seong

21) **목성** (Jupiter)
mok-seong

22) **토성** (Saturn)
to-seong

23) **천왕성** (Uranus)
cheon-wang-seong

24) **해왕성** (Neptune)
hae-wang-seong

밤에는 은하수 전체를 볼 수 있다.
At night, you can see the whole Milky Way Galaxy.

별똥별 본 적 있니?
Have you ever seen a shooting star?

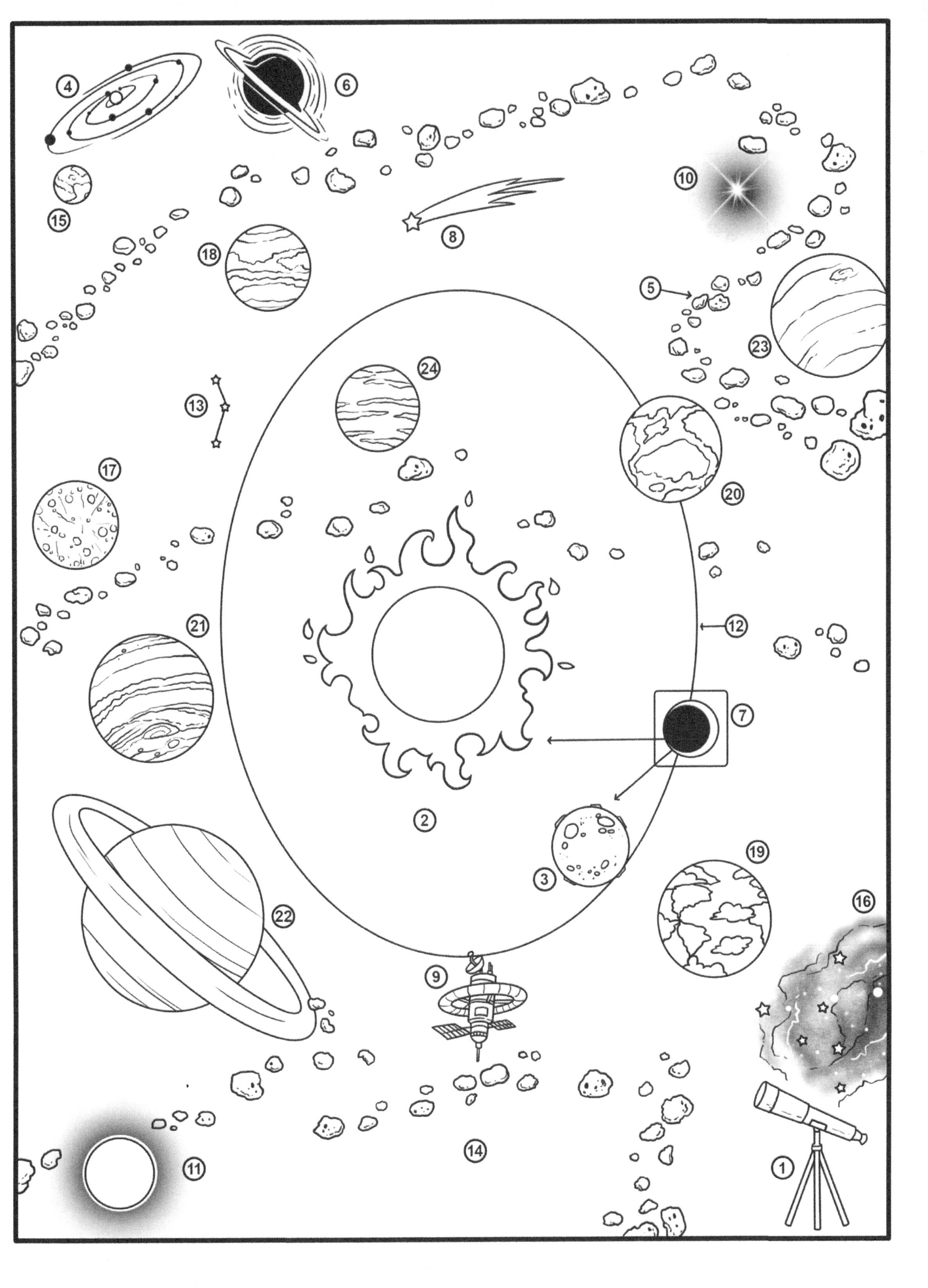

4
6
10
15
8
18
5
23
24
13
20
17
12
21
7
2
19
3
22
16
9
14
11
1

지리 (GEOGRAPHY)

1) **북, 북쪽** (north)
buk, buk-jjok

2) **동, 동쪽** (east)
dong, dong-jjok

3) **남, 남쪽** (south)
nam, nam-jjok

4) **서, 서쪽** (west)
seo, seo-jjok

5) **적도** (Equator)
jeok-do

6) **북회귀선** (Tropic of Cancer)
buk-hoe-gwi-seon

7) **남회귀선** (Tropic of Capricorn)
nam-hoe-gwi-seon

8) **남극** (South Pole)
nam-geuk

9) **북극** (North Pole)
buk-geuk

10) **북극권** (Arctic Circle)
buk-geuk-gwon

11) **대륙** (continent)
dae-ryuk

12) **해외에, 해외로** (overseas)
hae-oe-e, hae-oe-ro

13) **아프리카** (Africa)
Africa

14) **아시아** (Asia)
Asia

15) **북아메리카, 북미** (North America)
buk-*America*, buk-mi

16) **중앙 아메리카, 중미** (Central America)
jung-ang *America*, jung-mi

17) **남아메리카, 남미** (South America)
nam-*America*, nam-mi

18) **유럽** (Europe)
Europe

19) **오세아니아** (Oceania)
Oceania

20) **남극 대륙** (Antarctica)
nam-geuk dae-ryuk

21) **경선** (meridian)
gyeong-seon

22) **위선** (parallel)
wi-seon

23) **대서양** (Atlantic Ocean)
dae-seo-yang

24) **태평양** (Pacific Ocean)
tae-pyeong-yang

저는 한반도의 남쪽 지역에 살고 있어요.
I live in the south of the Korean peninsula.

우린 유럽 여행을 계획했어.
We have planned a trip to Europe.

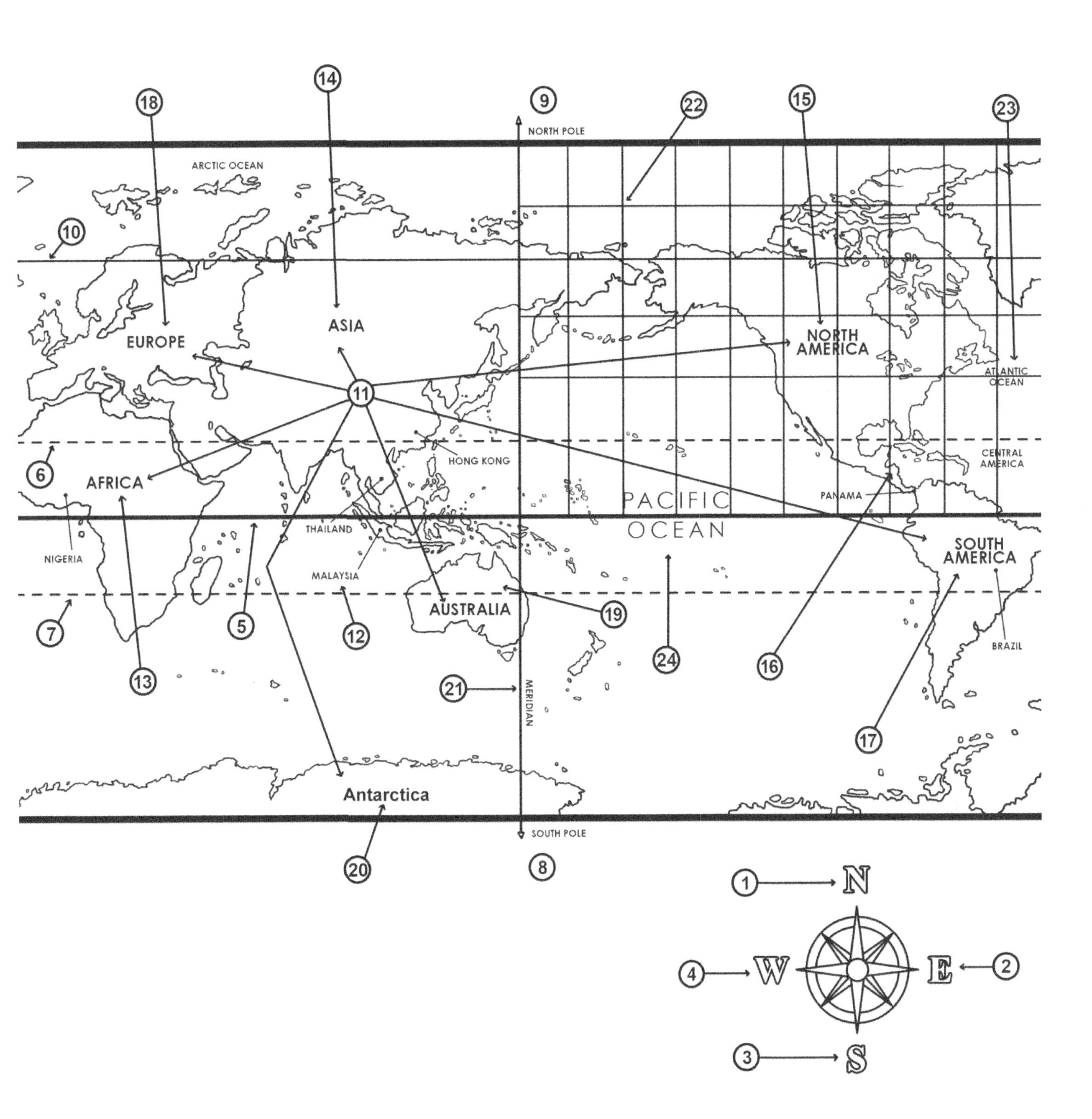

NORTH POLE
ARCTIC OCEAN
EUROPE
ASIA
NORTH AMERICA
ATLANTIC OCEAN
AFRICA
HONG KONG
CENTRAL AMERICA
PACIFIC OCEAN
PANAMA
THAILAND
NIGERIA
MALAYSIA
SOUTH AMERICA
AUSTRALIA
BRAZIL
MERIDIAN
Antarctica
SOUTH POLE
N
W
E
S
1
2
3
4
5
6
7
8
9
10
11
12
13
14
15
16
17
18
19
20
21
22
23
24

병원 (THE HOSPITAL)

1) **의사** (doctor/physician)
ui-sa

2) **간호사, 간호원** (nurse)
kan-ho-sa, kan-ho-won

3) **구급차** (ambulance)
ku-geup-cha

4) **응급처치함** (first-aid kit)
eung-geup-cheo-chi-ham

5) **체온계** (thermometer)
che-on-gye

6) **들것** (stretcher)
deul-geot

7) **주사기** (syringe)
ju-sa-gi

8) **바늘** (needle)
ba-neul

9) **청진기** (stethoscope)
cheong-jin-gi

10) **목발** (crutches)
mok-bal

11) **휠체어** (wheelchair)
hwil-*chair*

12) **관찰실** (observation room)
gwan-chal-shil

13) **병원 침대** (hospital bed)
byeong-won-chim-dae

14) **주사** (injection)
ju-sa

15) **수술** (surgery)
su-sul

16) **병력** (medical history)
byeong-reok

17) **환자** (patient)
hwan-ja

18) **알약, 정제** (pill/tablet)
al-lyak, jeong-je

수요일에 병원에 예약이 있어요.
I have an appointment at the hospital on Wednesday.

이 병원 침대는 불편하다.
This hospital bed is uncomfortable.

우리 딸은 간호사가 되고 싶어 한다.
My daughter wants to become a nurse.

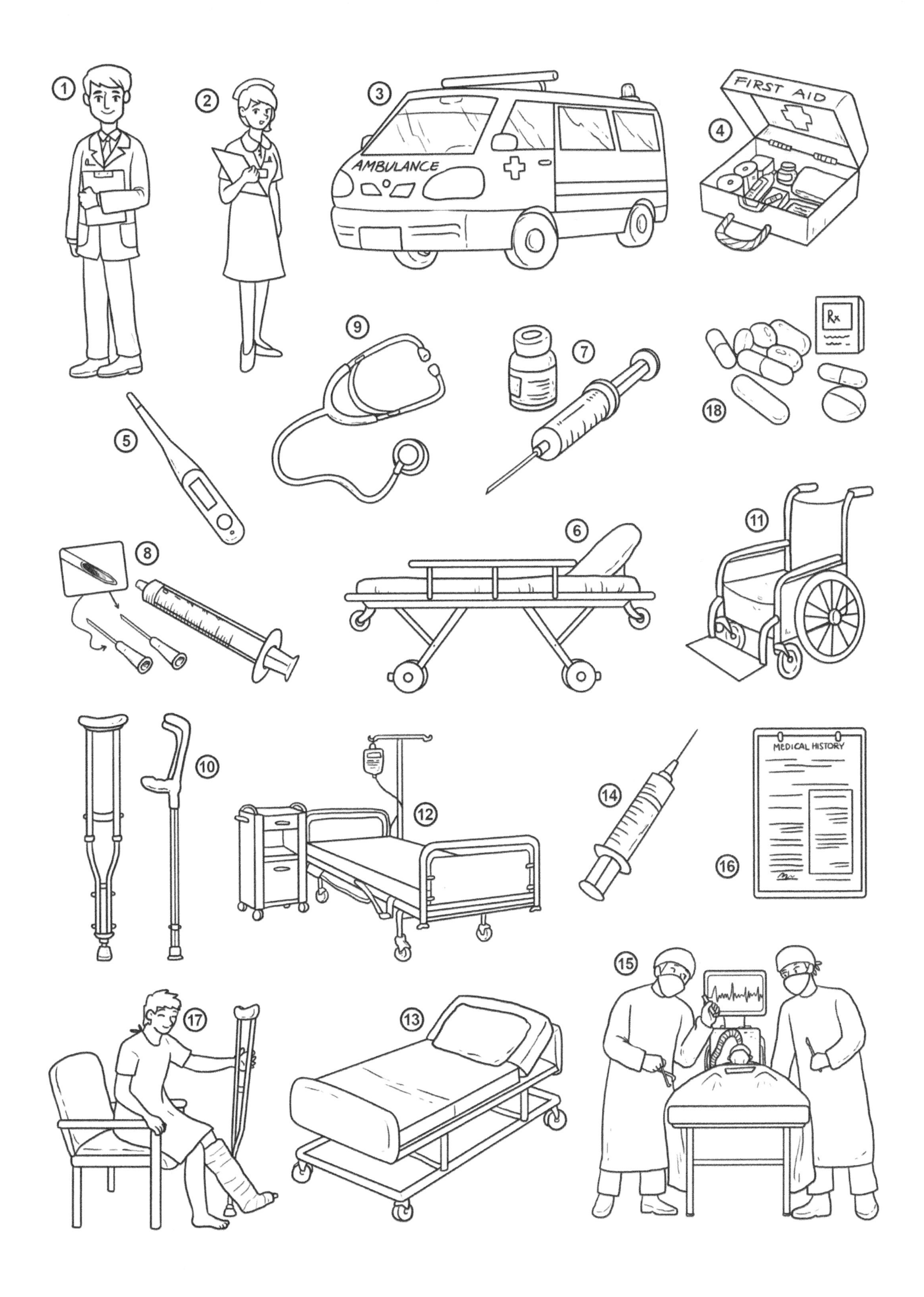

1
2
3
AMBULANCE
FIRST AID
4
Rx
9
7
18
5
6
11
8
10
12
14
MEDICAL HISTORY
16
15
17
13

농장 (THE FARM)

1) **헛간** (barn)
heot-gan

2) **마구간, 외양간** (cowshed/stable)
ma-gu-kkan, oe-yang-kkan

3) **농부** (farmer)
nong-gu

4) **쟁기** (plough)
jaeng-gi

5) **저장고** (silo)
jeo-jang-go

6) **방앗간** (mill)
bang-at-gan

7) **수조** (water trough)
su-jo

8) **닭장** (coop)
dak-jang

9) **벌집** (beehive)
beol-jjip

10) **건초 더미** (hay bale)
geon-cho tteo-mi

11) **소** (cattle)
so

12) **젖을 짜다** (to milk)
jeo-jeul jja-da

13) **떼** (herd/flock)
tte

14) **닭, 암탉** (fowl, hen)
dak, am-ttak

15) **우물** (well)
u-mul

16) **관개시설** (irrigation system)
gwan-gae-shi-seol

17) **허수아비** (scarecrow)
heo-su-a-bi

18) **흙길** (dirt road)
heuk-gil

우리 집 암탉은 하루에 12 개의 달걀을 낳는다.
My hens lay a dozen eggs per day.

새들을 쫓으려고 밭에 허수아비를 세웠다.
I installed a scarecrow in my field to scare birds away.

좌회전 한 후에 흙길을 따라가세요.
Turn left and follow the dirt road.

6
5
1
2
12
11
10
7
13
4
18
9
3
8
14
15
17
16

QUIZ #5

Use arrows to match the corresponding translations:

a. laboratory	1. USB 저장장치
b. pear	2. 휠체어
c. drums	3. 배
d. north	4. 콜리플라워
e. well	5. 딸기
f. bagpipes	6. 지구
g. wheelchair	7. 실험실
h. henhouse	8. 간호사
i. eggplant	9. 체리
j. nurse	10. 통계학
k. Earth	11. 백파이프
l. cauliflower	12. 우물
m. strawberry	13. 북쪽
n. flash drive	14. 가지
o. statistics	15. 드럼
p. cherry	16. 닭장

Fill in the blank spaces with the options below (use each word only once):

남편과 나는 주말에 시댁을 방문했어요. 시아버님의 _____가 고장이 나서 고쳐 드리러 갔어요. 시부모님께서는 시골에서 농사를 지으면서 살고 계세요. 상추도 심으시고, _____와 _____도 심으시죠. 닭장을 지어 놓고 그 안에서 _____도 여러 마리 키우고 계세요. 몇 년 전에 시골 땅에 직접 집을 짓고 살고 계시는데, 공기도 깨끗하고 밤엔 하늘에 ______도 많이 보여서 아주 좋아하세요. 시부모님 댁의 동쪽과 북쪽에는 산이 둘러져 있고, 남쪽과 _____은 탁 트여 있어서 전망도 아주 좋습니다. ______ 연주를 들으면서 멀리 산을 바라보고 있으면 멋진 카페에 온 것 같은 느낌이 들어요. 저도 언젠가는 _____로서의 삶을 꿈꿉니다.

별	서쪽
옥수수	컴퓨터
피아노	암탉
호박	농부

음식 (FOOD)

1) **포도** (grape)
   po-do
2) **호두** (walnut)
   ho-du
3) **고기** (meat)
   ko-gi
4) **양** (lamb)
   yang
5) **생선, 물고기** (fish)
   saeng-seon, mul-go-gi
6) **닭, 닭고기** (chicken)
   dak, dak-go-gi
7) **칠면조** (turkey)
   chil-myeon-jo
8) **꿀** (honey)
   kkul
9) **설탕** (sugar)
   seol-tang
10) **소금** (salt)
   so-geum
11) **후추** (black pepper)
   hu-chu
12) **베이컨** (bacon)
   bacon
13) **소시지** (sausage)
   sausage
14) **케첩** (ketchup)
   ketchup
15) **마요네즈** (mayonnaise)
   mayonnaise
16) **머스터드** (mustard)
   mustard
17) **잼** (jam)
   jam
18) **버터** (butter)
   butter
19) **주스** (juice)
   juice
20) **우유** (milk)
   u-yu

난 버터에 잼을 얹어 먹는 걸 좋아해.
I like to add jam to butter.

벌이 꿀을 만들어 낸다.
Bees make honey.

닭고기가 좋으세요, 아니면 생선이 좋으세요?
Do you prefer chicken or fish?

1
2
3
4
5
6
7
8
HONEY
9
SUGAR
10
S
11
P
12
13
14
KETCHUP
15
MAYONNAISE
16
MUSTARD
17
Jam
18
19
20

요리 (DISHES)

1) **라자냐** (lasagna)
   lasagna
2) **감자 오믈렛** (potato omelette)
   gam-ja *omelette*
3) **미트로프** (meatloaf)
   meatloaf
4) **볶음면** (fried noodles)
   bo-kkeum-myeon
5) **마카로니 치즈** (macaroni and cheese)
   macaroni cheese
6) **파에야** (paella)
   paella
7) **돼지갈비** (barbecued pork ribs)
   dwae-ji-gal-bi
8) **옥수수빵** (cornbread)
   ok-su-su-ppang
9) **스프링롤** (spring roll)
   spring roll
10) **치즈버거** (cheeseburger)
    cheeseburger
11) **후라이드 치킨, 닭튀김** (fried chicken)
    fried chicken, dak-twi-gim
12) **시저 샐러드** (Caesar salad)
    Caesar salad
13) **양파 수프** (onion soup)
    yang-pa *soup*
14) **코울슬로** (coleslaw)
    coleslaw
15) **양념 닭날개** (spicy chicken wings)
    yang-nyeom dang-nal-gae
16) **초코칩쿠키** (chocolate-chip cookies)
    chocochip cookie
17) **키라임 파이** (key lime pie)
    key lime pie
18) **치즈케이크** (cheesecake)
    cheesecake

한국 사람들은 후라이드 치킨을 진짜 좋아한다.
Koreans love fried chickens.

난 초코칩쿠키를 살 거야.
I am going to buy chocolate-chip cookies.

치즈케이크는 내가 가장 좋아하는 디저트이다.
Cheesecake is my favorite dessert.

1
2
3
4
5
6
7
8
9
10
11
12
13
14
15
16
17
18

해산물 (SEAFOOD)

1) **멸치** (anchovy)
myeol-chi

2) **대구** (cod)
dae-gu

3) **거미게** (spider crab)
keo-mi-ge

4) **고등어** (mackerel)
go-deung-eo

5) **랍스터** (lobster)
lobster

6) **가리비** (scallop)
ka-ri-bi

7) **도미** (snapper)
do-mi

8) **연어알** (salmon roe)
yeon-eo-al

9) **게** (crab)
ke

10) **조개류** (shellfish)
jo-gae-ryu

11) **장어** (eel)
jang-eo

12) **새우** (shrimp)
sae-u

한국 사람들은 국물을 낼 때 멸치를 자주 사용한다.
Koreans often use anchovies for fish stock.

고등어는 한국에서 가장 인기 있는 생선 중 하나이다.
Mackerels are one of the most popular fish in Korea.

난 연어를 간장에 찍어 먹는 걸 진짜 좋아한다.
I really like salmon dipped in soy sauce.

1
2
3
4
5
6
8
9
10
12
11
7

모양 (SHAPES)

1) **원, 동그라미** (circle)
won, dong-geu-ra-mi
2) **타원형** (oval)
ta-won-hyeong
3) **삼각형** (triangle)
sam-ga-kyeong
4) **직사각형** (rectangle)
jik-sa-ga-kyeong
5) **정사각형** (square)
jeong-sa-ga-kyeong
6) **사다리꼴** (trapezoid)
sa-da-ri-kkol
7) **마름모** (rhombus)
ma-reum-mo
8) **정육면체** (cube)
jeong-yung-myeon-che
9) **오각형** (pentagon)
o-ga-kyeong
10) **육각형** (hexagon)
yuk-ga-kyeong
11) **화살표** (arrow)
hwa-sal-pyo
12) **십자** (cross)
ship-ja
13) **하트** (heart)
heart
14) **별표** (star)
byeol-pyo
15) **원통** (cylinder)
won-tong
16) **원뿔** (cone)
won-ppul
17) **피라미드, 각뿔** (pyramid)
pyramid, gak-ppul
18) **구, 구체** (sphere)
ku, ku-che
19) **각기둥** (prism)
gak-ki-dung

하트 모양이 그려진 티셔츠 좋아해?
Do you like the shirt with heart shapes?

나는 한 번에 동그라미를 잘 못 그린다.
I can hardly draw a circle in one stroke.

이 쿠키는 원뿔 모양이다.
These cookies are in a cone shape.

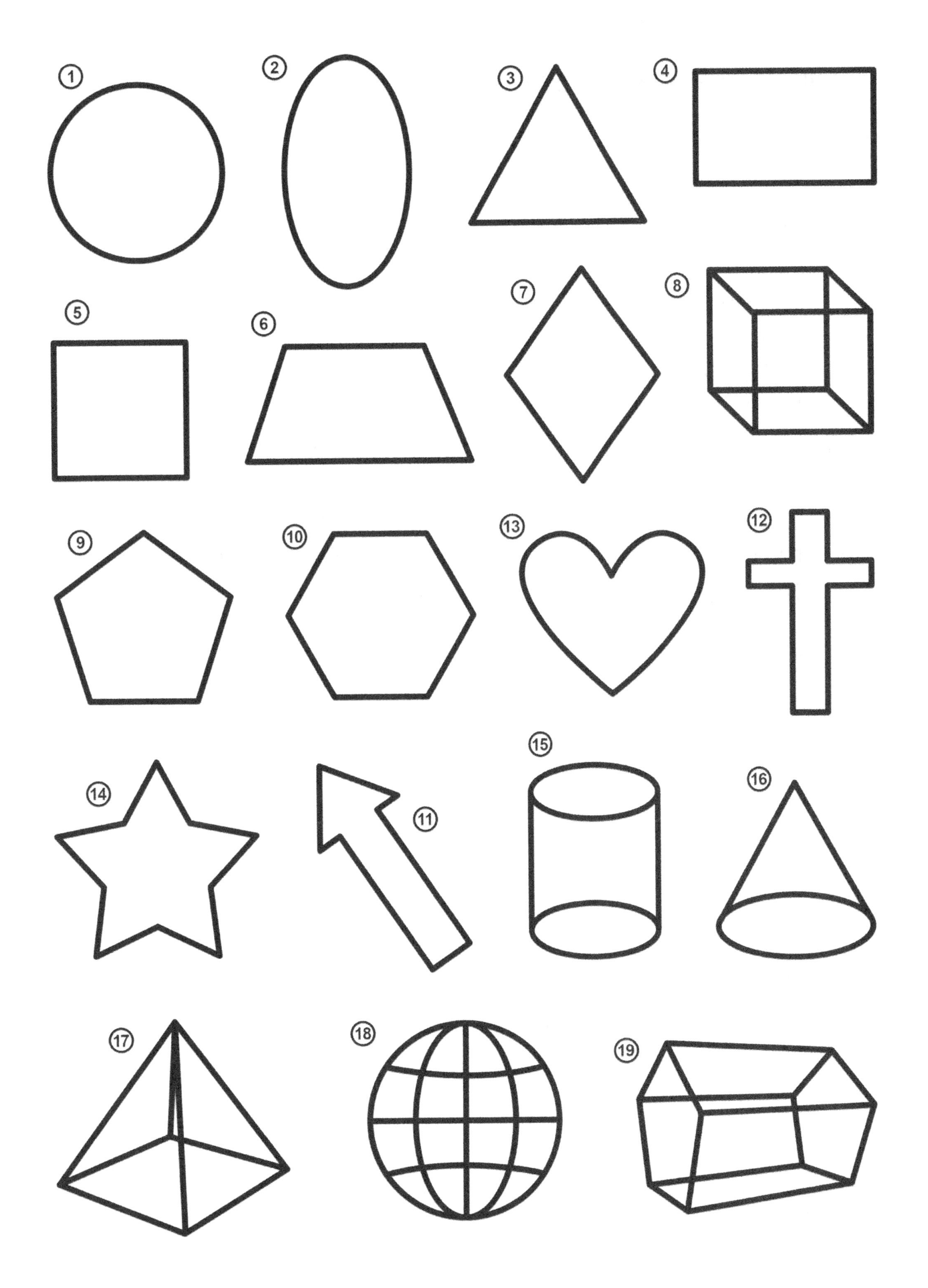

1
2
3
4
5
6
7
8
9
10
13
12
14
11
15
16
17
18
19

슈퍼마켓 (THE SUPERMARKET)

1) **쇼핑카트** (shopping cart)
shopping cart

2) **진열장** (cabinet/display case)
jin-yeol-jjang

3) **고객** (customer)
ko-gaek

4) **계산원, 캐셔** (cashier)
kye-san-won, *cashier*

5) **영수증** (receipt)
yeong-su-jeung

6) **빵집, 베이커리** (bakery)
ppang-jjip, *bakery*

7) **과일과 채소, 과채** (fruits and vegetables)
gwa-il-gwa chae-so, gwa-chae

8) **고기, 육류** (meat)
ko-gi, yung-nyu

9) **유제품** (dairy products)
yu-je-pum

10) **생선** (fish)
saeng-seon

11) **냉동식품** (frozen food)
naeng-dong-shik-pum

12) **가금류** (poultry)
ga-geum-nyu

13) **콩류** (legumes)
kong-nyu

14) **간식** (snacks)
kan-shik

15) **후식, 디저트** (dessert)
hu-shik, *dessert*

16) **음료수, 음료** (drinks)
eum-nyo-su, eum-nyo

17) **생활용품** (household items)
saeng-hwal-yong-pum

18) **컨베이어 벨트, 운반 벨트** (belt conveyor)
conveyor belt, un-ban *belt*

매일 아침 나는 빵집에서 빵을 산다.
I get my bread at the bakery every morning.

저는 채식주의자여서 고기는 안 먹어요.
I am a vegetarian; I do not eat meat.

이 가게는 신선한 과일과 채소를 팔아요.
This shop has fresh fruits and vegetables.

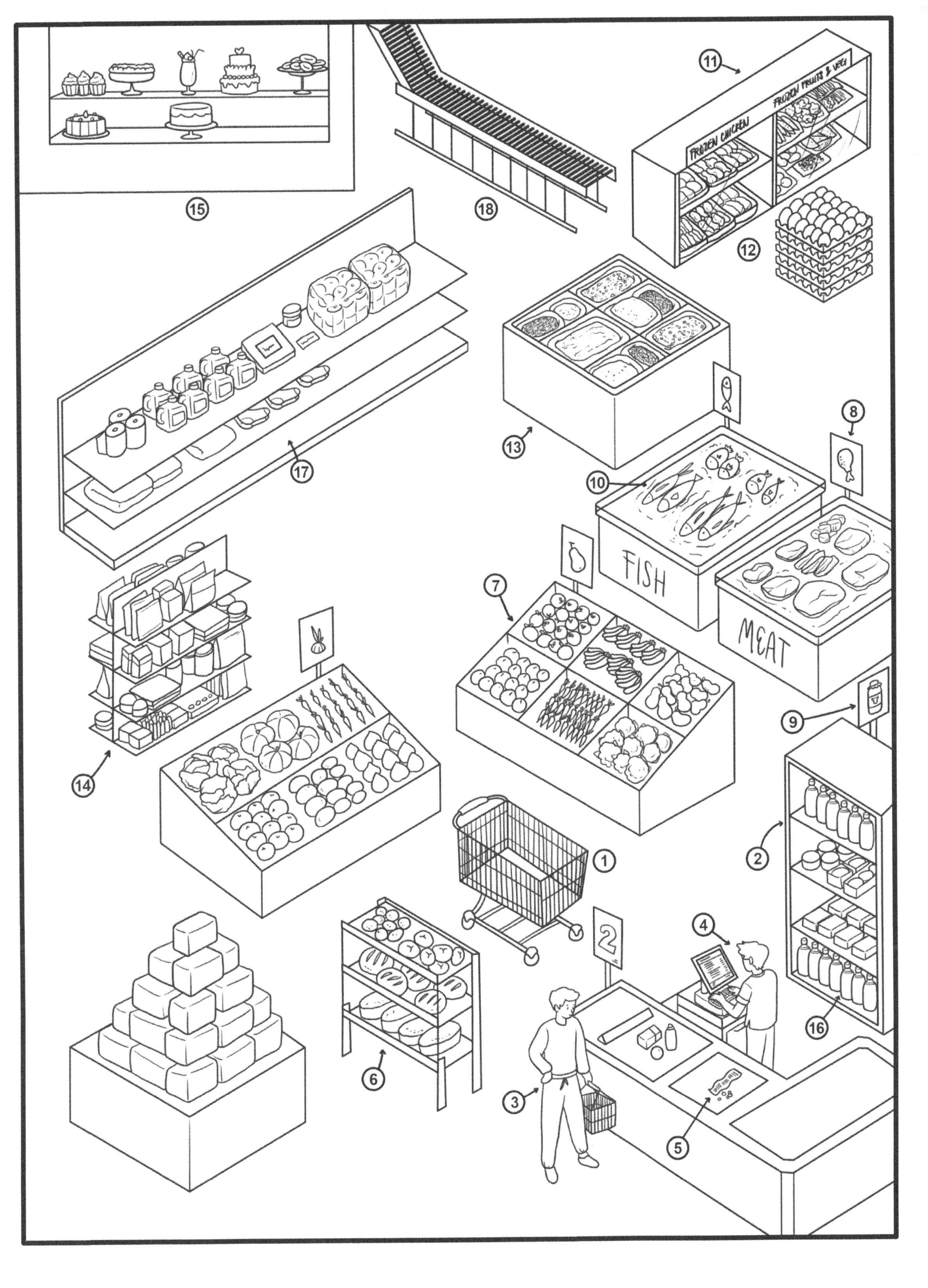
1
2
3
4
5
6
7
8
9
10
11
12
13
14
15
16
17
18
FROZEN CHICKEN
FROZEN FRUITS & VEG
FISH
MEAT
2

미디어 (MEDIA)

1) **잡지** (magazine)
   jap-ji
2) **팩스** (fax)
   fax
3) **신문** (journal)
   shin-mun
4) **우편물** (postal mail)
   u-pyeon-mul
5) **편지** (letter)
   pyeon-ji
6) **라디오** (radio)
   radio
7) **만화** (comic)
   man-hwa
8) **책, 도서, 서적** (book)
   chaek, do-seo, seo-jeok
9) **사진** (photography)
   sa-jin
10) **유선 전화** (landline phone)
    yu-seon-jeon-hwa
11) **텔레비전, TV** (television)
    television, TV
12) **영화** (movies)
    yeong-hwa
13) **핸드폰, 휴대폰, 휴대 전화** (mobile phone/cell phone)
    hand-phone, hyu-dae-*phone*, hyu-dae jeon-hwa
14) **수어** (sign language)
    su-eo

방탄소년단 콘서트가 내일 밤 TV 에서 방송한다.
BTS's concert airs on TV tomorrow night.

핸드폰 번호 줄 수 있으세요?
Can you give me your cell number?

나는 그에게 편지 한 통을 보냈다.
I have sent him a letter.

1
2
3
4
5
6
7
8
9
10
11
12
13
14
THE PAPER
Secret Garden
COMIC
ONE!
#1

축제 / 놀이공원 (THE FAIR/THE AMUSEMENT PARK)

1) **거울의 집** (house of mirrors)
keo-u-rui jip

2) **바이킹** (pirate ship/boat swing)
viking

3) **매표소** (ticket booth)
mae-pyo-so

4) **회전그네, 스윙 라이드** (swing ride)
hoe-jeon-geu-ne, *swing ride*

5) **롤러코스터** (roller coaster)
roller coaster

6) **페리스휠, 대관람차** (Ferris wheel)
Ferris wheel, dae-gwal-lam-cha

7) **회전목마** (carousel/merry-go-round)
hoe-jeon-mong-ma

8) **범퍼카** (bumper cars)
bumper car

9) **회전컵** (teacups/cup and saucer)
hoe-jeon-*cup*

10) **바이킹** (pendulum)
viking

11) **오락실** (arcade room)
o-rak-shil

12) **핫도그** (corn dog)
hot dog

13) **스노콘** (snow cone)
snow cone

14) **솜사탕** (cotton candy)
som-sa-tang

15) **캔디 애플** (candy apple)
candy apple

난 롤러코스터 진짜 좋아!
I love roller coasters!

그는 거울의 집에서 길을 잃었다.
He got lost in the house of mirrors.

난 솜사탕을 너무 많이 먹었어.
I ate too much cotton candy.

HOUSE OF MIRRORS
TICKET
ARCADE
ME
GAME
1
2
3
4
5
6
7
8
9
10
11
12
13
14
15

중요한 사건 (LIFE EVENTS)

1) **출생, 탄생** (birth)
chul-saeng, tan-saeng

2) **세례** (christening/baptism)
se-rye

3) **학교 첫 날, 입학** (first day of school)
hak-kyo cheon nal, i-pak

4) **친구를 사귀다** (make friends)
chin-gu-reul sa-gwi-da

5) **생일, 생신** (birthday)
saeng-il, saeng-shin

6) **사랑에 빠지다** (fall in love)
sa-rang-e ppa-ji-da

7) **졸업** (graduation)
jo-reop

8) **대학교에 입학하다** (to start university/begin college)
dae-hak-kyo-e i-pa-ka-da

9) **직장을 구하다** (get a job)
jik-jang-eul ku-ha-da

10) **사업가가 되다** (become an entrepreneur)
sa-eop-ga-ga doe-da

11) **세계 여행을 하다** (travel around the world)
se-gye yeo-haeng-eul ha-da

12) **결혼하다** (get married)
gyeol-hon-ha-da

13) **아기를 갖다** (have a baby)
a-ki-reul gat-da

14) **생일을 축하하다, 생일을 기념하다** (celebrate a birthday)
saeng-il-eul chu-ka-ha-da, saeng-il-eul ki-nyeom-ha-da

15) **은퇴** (retirement)
eun-toe

16) **죽음, 사망** (death)
ju-geum, sa-mang

나 다음 달에 결혼해.
I am going to get married next month.

우리 부모님은 은퇴하셨어.
My parents are retired.

그는 결국 직장을 구했어.
He has finally found a job.

1
2
3
4
5
6
7
8
9
10
11
12
13
14
15
16

형용사 I (ADJECTIVES I)

1) **크다** (big)
keu-da

2) **작다** (small)
jak-da

3) **시끄럽다, 소리가 크다** (loud)
shi-kkeu-reop-da, so-ri-ga keu-da

4) **조용하다** (silent)
jo-yong-ha-da

5) **길다** (long)
gil-da

6) **짧다** (short)
jjal-tta

7) **넓다** (wide)
neol-tta

8) **좁다** (narrow)
jop-da

9) **비싸다** (expensive)
bi-ssa-da

10) **싸다** (cheap)
ssa-da

11) **빠르다** (fast)
ppa-reu-da

12) **느리다** (slow)
neu-ri-da

13) **비어 있다** (empty)
bi-eo it-da

14) **가득차다, 가득하다** (full)
ga-deuk-cha-da, ga-deu-ka-da

15) **부드럽다** (soft)
bu-deu-reop-da

16) **딱딱하다, 단단하다** (hard)
ttak-tta-ka-da, dan-dan-ha-da

17) **크다, 키가 크다** (tall)
keu-da, ki-ga keu-da

18) **작다, 키가 작다** (short)
jak-da, ki-ga jak-da

이웃 집 강아지는 정말 시끄럽다.
The neighbor's dog is very loud.

이 식당은 맛도 좋고 값도 싸다.
This restaurant is good and cheap.

치타는 가장 빠른 동물이다.
The cheetah is the fastest animal.

3
4
2
1
7
8
5
6
12
11
9
10
15
16
13
14
17
18

QUIZ #6

Use arrows to match the corresponding translations:

a. book	1. 음료수
b. dairy products	2. 장어
c. roller coaster	3. 호두
d. eel	4. 생선
e. circle	5. 양파 수프
f. anchovy	6. 칠면조
g. jam	7. 유제품
h. cotton candy	8. 십자
i. carousel	9. 롤러코스터
j. turkey	10. 회전목마
k. drinks	11. 책
l. cross	12. 잼
m. walnut	13. 솜사탕
n. fish	14. 멸치
o. onion soup	15. 동그라미

Fill in the blank spaces with the options below (use each word only once):

오늘은 정말 기쁜 날이에요. 유민 씨의 동생 유리 씨가 대학교에 ___한 날이기 때문이죠. 온 가족이 모여서 맛있는 저녁 식사를 하기로 했습니다. 유리 씨는 생선을 좋아하기 때문에 _____ 구이를 할 거예요. 그리고 후라이드 치킨과 ______도 준비했습니다. ____으로는 과일을 내놓을 거예요. 유리 씨가 좋아하는 ____와 딸기를 미리 사놓았죠. 유리 씨는 대학교에서 경영학을 전공하고 _____가 되고 싶어 해요. 유민 씨는 동생의 꿈을 늘 응원한다고 ____에 써서 선물과 함께 줬습니다. 그리고 가족이 모두 이 기쁜 날을 기념하기 위해 핸드폰으로 ___도 찍었어요.

후식	고등어
편지	사진
돼지갈비	사업가
입학	포도

형용사 II (ADJECTIVES II)

1) **새롭다** (new)
   sae-rop-da
2) **오래되다** (old)
   o-rae-doe-da
3) **편안하다** (comfortable)
   pyeo-nan-ha-da
4) **불편하다** (uncomfortable)
   bul-pyeon-ha-da
5) **위험하다** (dangerous)
   wi-heom-ha-da
6) **성가시다** (annoying)
   seong-ga-shi-da
7) **불안하다** (anxious, insecure)
   bul-an-ha-da
8) **완전하다** (complete)
   wan-jeon-ha-da
9) **불완전하다** (incomplete)
   bul-wan-jeon-ha-da
10) **부러지다** (broken)
   bu-reo-ji-da
11) **멋지다** (gorgeous)
   meot-ji-da
12) **고결하다** (virtuous)
   go-gyeol-ha-da
13) **비슷하다** (similar)
   bi-seu-ta-da
14) **다르다** (different)
   da-reu-da
15) **열려 있다, (눈을) 뜨고 있다** (open)
   yeol-lyeo it-da, (nun-eul) tteu-go it-da
16) **닫혀 있다, (눈을) 감고 있다** (closed)
   da-cheo it-da, (nun-eul) gam-kko it-da

그 쌍둥이는 정말 비슷하다.
Those twins are very similar.

내 소파는 오래됐지만 편안하다.
My sofa is old but comfortable.

이 가게는 절대 안 열려 있네!
This shop is never open!

5
DANGER
HIGH VOLTAGE
4
1
2
6
3
7
8
9
11
10
12
14
13
15
16

부사 (ADVERBS)

1) **여기에** (here)
yeo-gi-e

2) **저기에** (there)
jeo-gi-e

3) **근처에** (near)
geun-cheo-e

4) **멀리** (far)
meol-li

5) **위로** (up)
wi-ro

6) **아래로** (down)
a-rae-ro

7) **안에** (inside)
an-e

8) **밖에** (outside)
ba-kke

9) **앞에** (ahead)
ap-e

10) **뒤에** (behind)
dwi-e

11) **아니, 아니요** (no)
a-ni, a-ni-yo

12) **응, 네** (yes)
eung, ne

13) **지금** (now)
ji-geum

14) **잘** (well/good/right)
jal

15) **잘못** (bad/wrong)
jal-mot

난 산책하러 밖에 나갔다.
I went outside for a walk.

지금 나한테 전화해.
Call me now.

누군가 여기에 있어요.
Somebody is here.

1
2
4
3
5
6
7
8
9
10
11
12
13
14
15

길 찾기 (DIRECTIONS)

1) **블록** (block)
block

2) **광장** (square)
gwang-jang

3) **공원** (park)
gong-won

4) **지하철** (subway)
ji-ha-cheol

5) **모퉁이** (corner)
mo-tung-i

6) **거리** (avenue)
keo-ri

7) **길** (street)
kil

8) **버스 정류장** (bus stop)
bus jeong-nyu-jang

9) **신호등** (traffic lights)
shin-ho-deung

10) **횡단보도** (crossing/crosswalk)
hoeng-dan-bo-do

11) **위로** (up)
wi-ro

12) **아래로** (down)
a-rae-ro

13) **왼쪽** (left)
oen-jjok

14) **오른쪽** (right)
o-reun-jjok

15) **도로 표지판** (road signs)
do-ro pyo-ji-pan

16) **교통 경찰** (traffic police)
kyo-tong gyeong-chal

서울은 지하철 시스템이 편리하다.
The subway system is convenient in Seoul.

왼쪽에 은행이 보일 겁니다.
You will see the bank on the left.

횡단보도가 저기에 있어요.
The crosswalk is over there.

5TH AVENUE
2ND AVENUE
PUBLIC
SQUARE STREET
1ST AVENUE
West ST
BUS STOP
WELCOME
TO THE PARK
1
2
3
4
5
6
7
8
9
10
11
12
13
14
15
16

식당 (THE RESTAURANT)

1) **매니저** (manager)
   manager
2) **테이블** (table)
   table
3) **메뉴판** (menu)
   menu-pan
4) **요리** (dish)
   yo-ri
5) **애피타이저** (appetizer)
   appetizer
6) **전채 요리** (starter)
   jeon-chae yo-ri
7) **주 요리, 메인 코스** (main course)
   ju yo-ri, *main course*
8) **후식, 디저트** (dessert)
   hu-shik, *dessert*
9) **식당 손님** (diner)
   shik-dang son-nim
10) **요리사** (cook)
   yo-ri-sa
11) **종업원** (waiter)
   jong-eo-bwon
12) **종업원** (waitress)
   jong-eo-bwon
13) **팁** (tip)
   tip
14) **높은 의자** (high chair)
   no-peun ui-ja
15) **와인 리스트** (wine list)
   wine list
16) **파티시에** (pastry chef)
   pâtissier

저희 메뉴판 보시겠어요?
Would you like to see our menu?

전 후식을 먹을게요.
I will have dessert please.

높은 의자 하나만 갖다 주시겠어요?
Could you bring us a high chair?

1
2
3
4
5
6
7
8
9
10
11
12
13
14
15
16
Wine List
Menu

쇼핑몰 (THE MALL)

1) **층** (floor)
cheung

2) **아쿠아리움** (aquarium)
aquarium

3) **푸드코트** (food court)
food court

4) **엘리베이터** (elevator)
elevator

5) **에스컬레이터** (escalator)
escalator

6) **비상구** (emergency exit)
bi-sang-gu

7) **미용실** (beauty salon)
mi-yong-shil

8) **옷 가게** (clothing store)
ot ka-ge

9) **놀이터** (playground)
no-ri-teo

10) **보안 요원** (security guard)
bo-an yo-won

11) **감시 카메라** (surveillance camera)
gam-shi *camera*

12) **빵집, 베이커리** (bakery)
ppang-jip, *bakery*

13) **스포츠용품점** (sporting goods store)
sports-yong-pum-jeom

14) **분수대** (fountain)
bun-su-dae

엘리베이터를 타고 2 층에서 내리세요.
Take the elevator and stop on the second floor.

난 우리 딸을 미용실에 데려갈 거야.
I am going to take my daughter to the beauty salon.

이 쇼핑몰에 빵집이 어디 있죠?
Where is the bakery in this mall?

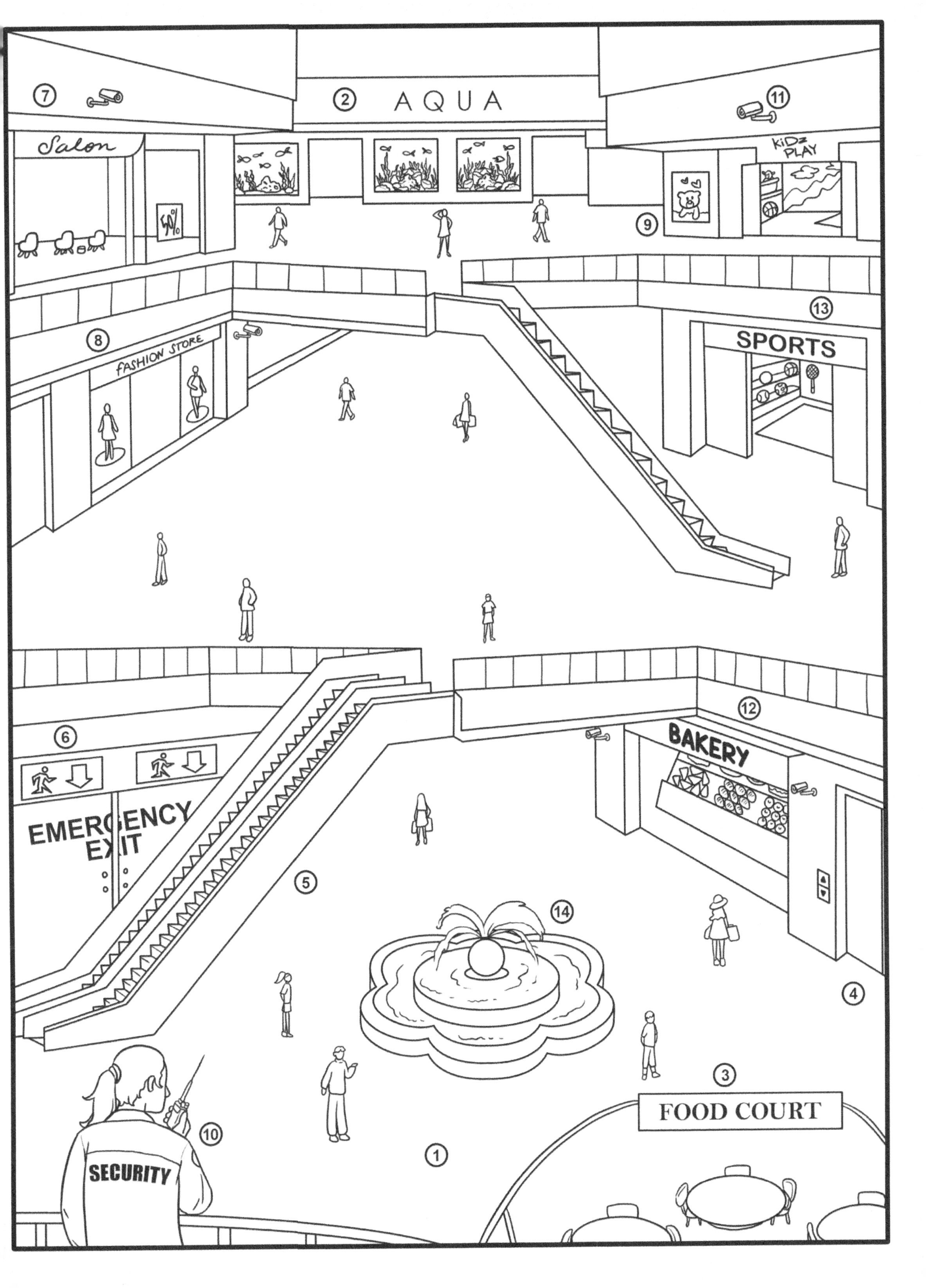

7
2
AQUA
11
Salon
KiDz PLAY
50%
9
8
FASHION STORE
13
SPORTS
6
12
BAKERY
EMERGENCY EXIT
5
14
4
3
FOOD COURT
10
SECURITY
1

동사 I (VERBS I)

1) **말하다** (to talk)
mal-ha-da

2) **마시다** (to drink)
ma-shi-da

3) **먹다** (to eat)
meok-da

4) **걷다** (to walk)
keot-da

5) **열다** (to open)
yeol-da

6) **닫다** (to close)
dat-da

7) **주다** (to give)
ju-da

8) **보다** (to see)
bo-da

9) **따라가다** (to follow)
tta-ra-ga-da

10) **안다** (to hug)
an-tta

11) **키스하다** (to kiss)
kiss-ha-da

12) **사다** (to buy)
sa-da

13) **듣다** (to listen)
deut-da

14) **노래하다** (to sing)
no-rae-ha-da

15) **춤추다** (to dance)
chum-chu-da

창문은 닫아야 해요.
You must close the window.

그를 따라가면 돼.
You can follow him.

난 아침에 주로 팟캐스트를 듣는다.
I usually listen to the podcast in the morning.

동사 II (VERBS II)

1) **쓰다** (to write)
   sseu-da
2) **읽다** (to read)
   ik-da
3) **청소하다** (to clean)
   cheong-so-ha-da
4) **줍다** (to pick up)
   jup-da
5) **찾다** (to find)
   chat-da
6) **씻다** (to wash)
   ssit-da
7) **보다** (to watch)
   bo-da
8) **고치다** (to fix)
   go-chi-da
9) **생각하다** (to think)
   saeng-ga-ka-da
10) **찍다** (to take)
    jjik-da
11) **자르다** (to cut)
    ja-reu-da
12) **멈추다** (to stop)
    meom-chu-da
13) **울다** (to cry)
    ul-da
14) **웃다** (to smile)
    ut-da
15) **도와주다** (to help)
    do-wa-ju-da

나는 TV 에서 한국 드라마 보는 것을 좋아해.
I like watching Korean dramas on TV.

난 내 방을 청소할 거야.
I am going to clean my room.

난 우리 집 강아지가 똑똑하다고 생각해.
I think my puppy is smart.

1
2
3
5
4
6
7
8
9
10
11
STOP
12
13
14
15

건축 I (CONSTRUCTION I)

1) **크레인** (crane)
crane

2) **위험 테이프** (hazard tape)
wi-heom *tape*

3) **트래픽 콘** (traffic cone)
traffic cone

4) **공사용 삽** (construction shovel)
gong-sa-yong sap

5) **망치** (hammer)
mang-chi

6) **철사 절단기** (wire cutters)
cheol-sa jeol-ttan-gi

7) **페인트 롤러** (paint roller)
paint roller

8) **전기톱** (chainsaw)
jeon-gi-top

9) **드릴** (drill)
drill

10) **소형 착암기** (jackhammer)
so-hyeong cha-gam-gi

11) **펜치** (pliers)
pen-chi

12) **드라이버** (screwdriver)
driver

너네 집에 펜치 있니?
Do you have pliers in your house?

이 그림 걸려면 망치가 필요해.
I need a hammer to hang this picture.

그 드라이버 좀 줘.
Give me the screwdriver.

1
2
3
4
5
6
7
8
9
10
11
12

건축 II (CONSTRUCTION II)

1) **공구함** (toolbox)
gong-gu-ham

2) **헬멧** (work helmet/hard hat)
helmet

3) **도면** (blueprint)
do-myeon

4) **파이프** (pipes)
pipe

5) **모종삽** (trowel)
mo-jong-sap

6) **콘크리트 믹서기** (concrete mixer)
concrete mixer-gi

7) **벽돌** (brick)
byeok-dol

8) **건축 자재** (building materials)
keon-chuk ja-jae

9) **타일** (tiles)
tile

10) **시멘트** (cement)
cement

11) **모래** (sand)
mo-rae

12) **자갈** (gravel)
ja-gal

여기 집들은 벽돌로 지어졌다.
These houses are made of bricks.

내 공구함이 차고 안에 있다.
My toolbox is in the garage.

이 건물의 도면을 가지고 계세요?
Do you have the blueprint for this building?

8
9
12
10
6
3
4
2
7
11
5
1

QUIZ #7

Use arrows to match the corresponding translations:

a. waitress	1. 말하다
b. left	2. 열려 있다
c. old	3. 멀리
d. bus stop	4. 노래하다
e. wrong	5. 오른쪽
f. playground	6. 놀이터
g. right	7. 엘리베이터
h. to talk	8. 빵집
i. main course	9. 닫혀 있다
j. closed	10. 사다
k. to sing	11. 왼쪽
l. elevator	12. 잘못
m. to buy	13. 오래되다
n. open	14. 종업원
o. bakery	15. 버스 정류장
p. far	16. 주 요리

Fill in the blank spaces with the options below (use each word only once):

여기서 지하철 역으로 가는 길을 알려 드릴게요. 먼저 이 ________를 따라 10 분 정도 걸어 가세요. 그럼 ________에 공원이 보일 거예요. 거기서 __________로 길을 건너세요. 그러고 나서 왼쪽으로 가다 보면 ______________이 나와요. 그 근처에는 빵집과 미용실이 있죠. 거기서 두 _________ 더 가면 지하철 역에 도착합니다. 지하철 역 앞에 큰 _________________가 있어서 찾기 쉬울 거예요. 타는 곳은 ______________를 타고 지하 2_____까지 가면 돼요.

블록

분수대

에스컬레이터

횡단보도

층

거리

오른쪽

버스 정류장

풀과 나무 (PLANTS AND TREES)

1) **야생화** (wildflower)
ya-saeng-hwa

2) **허브** (herb)
heo-beu

3) **버섯** (mushroom)
beo-seot

4) **잡초** (weed)
jap-cho

5) **해초** (seaweed)
hae-cho

6) **고사리** (fern)
go-sa-ri

7) **갈대** (reed)
gal-ttae

8) **대나무** (bamboo)
dae-na-mu

9) **담쟁이덩굴** (ivy)
dam-jaeng-i-deong-gul

10) **이끼** (moss)
i-kki

11) **풀** (grass)
pul

12) **야자나무** (palm tree)
ya-ja-na-mu

13) **맹그로브** (mangrove)
mangrove

14) **선인장** (cactus)
seo-nin-jang

그는 내게 야생화 한 다발을 선물해 줬다.
He gave me a bouquet of wildflowers as a gift.

대나무는 정말 빨리 자란다.
Bamboo grows very fast.

오늘 밤, 우린 버섯 파스타를 먹을 거야.
Tonight, we are having mushroom pasta.

12
14
7
9
13
8
6
10
4
3
1
2
11
5

축제 (THE CARNIVAL)

1) **가면** (mask)
ga-myeon

2) **변장** (costume/disguise)
byeon-jang

3) **장식 차량** (float)
jang-shik cha-ryang

4) **꽃** (flowers)
kkot

5) **작은북** (snare drum)
ja-geun-buk

6) **광대** (clown)
gwang-dae

7) **슈퍼히어로** (superhero)
superhero

8) **공주** (princess)
gong-ju

9) **우주 비행사** (astronaut)
u-ju bi-haeng-sa

10) **마임** (mime)
mime

11) **죄수** (prisoner)
joe-su

12) **가전제품** (household appliance)
ga-jeon-je-pum

13) **요정** (fairy)
yo-jeong

14) **나무꾼** (lumberjack)
na-mu-kkun

나는 내 자동차를 꽃들로 장식했다.
I decorated my car with flowers.

너는 이 파티에서 가면을 써야 한다.
You must wear a mask at this party.

그녀는 마치 공주같다.
She looks like a princess.

3
13
12
11
9
8
7
6
5
10
4
1
2
14

공방 (THE WORKSHOP)

1) **도구** (tool)
   do-gu
2) **마구 제조술** (saddlery)
   ma-gu je-jo-sul
3) **목공일** (carpentry/woodwork)
   mok-gong-nil
4) **천갈이** (upholstery/tapestry)
   cheon-ga-ri
5) **구두 제작수선** (shoemaking/shoe repair)
   gu-du je-jak-su-seon
6) **은세공인** (silversmith)
   eun-se-gong-in
7) **대장장이** (blacksmith)
   dae-jang-jang-i
8) **정비공** (mechanic)
   jeong-bi-gong
9) **직물** (textile)
   jing-mul
10) **제빵** (bakery)
    je-ppang
11) **모조 장신구** (costume jewelry)
    mo-jo jang-shin-gu
12) **신발** (footwear)
    shin-bal
13) **유지 보수** (maintenance)
    yu-ji bo-su
14) **수리** (repair)
    su-ri
15) **회화** (painting)
    hoe-hwa
16) **제과** (pastry)
    je-gwa

그 정비공은 내 차 수리를 끝냈다.
The mechanic has finished repairing my car.

이 도구는 뭐 하는 거지?
What is this tool for?

우리는 목공일 같은 실질적인 기술을 가진 사람들이 필요하다.
We need people with practical skills like carpentry.

1
2
3
4
5
6
7
8
9
10
11
12
13
14
15
16

식료품점 (THE GROCERY STORE)

1) **파스타** (pasta)
pasta

2) **쌀** (rice)
ssal

3) **귀리** (oat)
gwi-ri

4) **빵** (bread)
pão

5) **기름** (oils)
ki-reum

6) **소스** (sauces)
sauce

7) **샐러드 드레싱** (salad dressings)
salad dressing

8) **조미료** (condiments)
jo-mi-ryo

9) **통조림 제품** (canned goods)
tong-jo-rim je-pum

10) **햄** (ham)
ham

11) **치즈** (cheese)
cheese

12) **땅콩 버터** (peanut butter)
ttang-kong *butter*

13) **사탕** (candy)
sa-tang

14) **콩류** (beans)
kong-nyu

15) **커피** (coffee)
coffee

16) **차** (tea)
cha

난 참기름이랑 고추장을 사고 싶어.
I want to buy sesame oil and hot pepper paste.

넌 집에 조미료 많이 갖고 있니?
Do you have lots of condiments at home?

쌀은 한국인들에게 가장 중요한 주식이다.
Rice is one of the most important staple foods for Koreans.

10
2
ICE
RICE
RICE
RICE
16
13
8
7
15
COFFEE
COFFEE
9
12
6
5
11
1
4
3
OATS
OATS
14

여행과 생활 I (TRAVEL AND LIVING I)

1) **집주인** (host/hostess)
   jip-ju-in
2) **관광객** (tourist)
   gwan-gwang-gaek
3) **여행객** (traveler)
   yeo-haeng-gaek
4) **수하물** (luggage)
   su-ha-mul
5) **휴대 가능 수하물** (hand luggage)
   hyu-dae ga-neung su-ha-mul
6) **카메라** (camera)
   camera
7) **호텔** (hotel)
   hotel
8) **호스텔** (hostel)
   hostel
9) **민박 / 여관** (Bed & Breakfast/inn)
   min-bak / yeo-gwan
10) **객실** (cabin)
    gaek-shil
11) **텐트** (tent)
    tent
12) **비행기** (flight)
    bi-haeng-gi
13) **출발** (departure)
    chul-bal
14) **도착** (arrival)
    do-chak

난 호텔에 3 박을 예약했다.
I booked a hotel for three nights.

비행기는 오후 1 시 30 분에 출발합니다.
The flight departs at 1:30 p.m.

카메라 까먹지 마!
Do not forget the camera!

12
7
13
10
8
14
HOTEL
HOSTEL
1
2
9
inn
3
6
11
5
4

여행과 생활 II (TRAVEL AND LIVING II)

1) **마을** (town)
ma-eul

2) **지도** (map)
ji-do

3) **버스 정류장** (bus stop)
bus jeong-nyu-jang

4) **택시** (taxi)
taxi

5) **차량 대여** (car rental)
cha-ryang dae-yeo

6) **기차역** (train station)
ki-cha-yeok

7) **공항** (airport)
gong-hang

8) **여권** (passport)
yeo-kkwon

9) **신분증** (ID/identification card)
shin-bun-jjeung

10) **현지 통화** (currency)
hyeon-ji tong-hwa

11) **현금** (cash)
hyeon-geum

12) **직불 카드** (debit card)
jik-bul *card*

13) **신용 카드** (credit card)
shi-nyong *card*

14) **관광 가이드** (tourist guide)
gwan-gwang *guide*

난 여권을 갱신해야 돼.
I must renew my passport.

신용 카드 아니면 현금으로 지불하시나요?
Are you paying by credit card or cash?

절 위해 택시를 예약해 주시겠어요?
Could you book a taxi for me?

TOWN
CAR REN
TRAIN STATION
EXCHANGE OFFICE
TAXI
Passport
CREDIT CARD
DEBIT CARD
1
2
3
4
5
6
7
8
9
10
11
12
13
14

장난감 (TOYS)

1) **공** (ball)
   gong
2) **곰 인형** (teddy bear)
   gom in-hyeong
3) **기차** (train)
   ki-cha
4) **스케이트보드** (skateboard)
   skateboard
5) **인형** (doll)
   in-hyeong
6) **레이싱 카** (race car)
   racing car
7) **로봇** (robot)
   robot
8) **연** (kite)
   yeon
9) **드럼** (drum)
   drum
10) **훌라후프** (hula hoop)
   hula hoop
11) **수레** (wagon)
   su-re
12) **블록** (blocks)
   block
13) **실로폰** (xylophone)
   xylophone
14) **트럭** (truck)
   truck
15) **비행기** (airplane)
   bi-haeng-gi
16) **블록** (bricks)
   block

저는 10 년 전에 드럼 치는 법을 배웠어요.
I learned to play the drums 10 years ago.

우리 딸이 곰 인형을 잃어버렸어요.
My daughter has lost her teddy bear.

나한테 공 던져줘!
Throw me the ball!

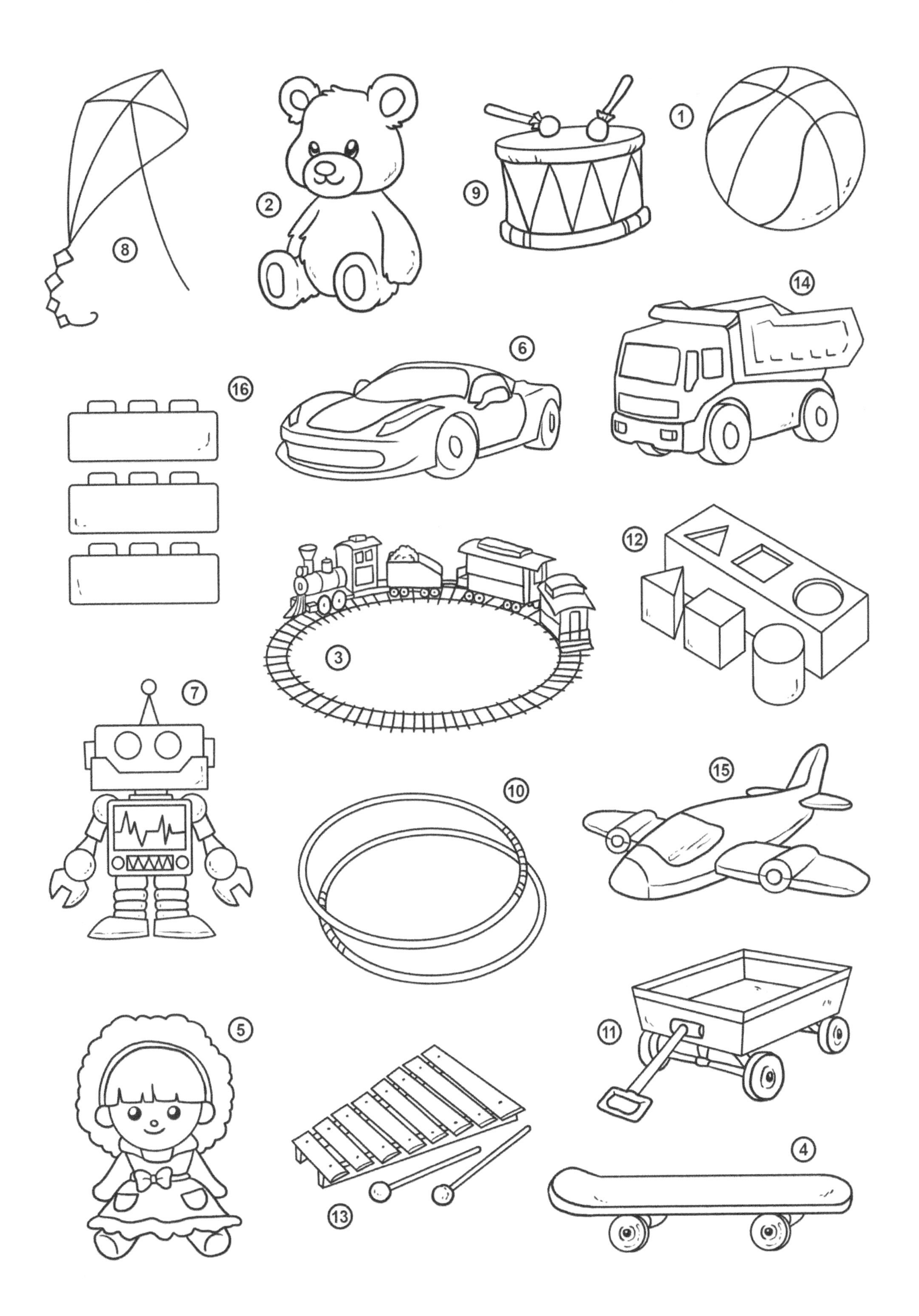
1
9
2
8
14
6
16
12
3
7
15
10
5
11
4
13

생일 잔치 (THE BIRTHDAY PARTY)

1) **생일 현수막** (birthday banner)
saeng-il hyeon-su-mak

2) **장식** (decoration)
jang-shik

3) **선물** (present/gift)
seon-mul

4) **식기류** (tableware)
shik-gi-ryu

5) **생일을 맞은 사람** (birthday person)
saeng-i-reul ma-jeun sa-ram

6) **풍선** (balloon)
pung-seon

7) **생일 케이크** (birthday cake)
saeng-il *cake*

8) **접시** (plates)
jeop-shi

9) **포크** (fork)
fork

10) **숟가락, 스푼** (spoons)
sut-ka-rak, *spoon*

11) **컵** (cups)
cup

12) **빨대** (straw)
ppal-ttae

13) **피냐타** (piñata)
piñata

14) **초** (candle)
cho

15) **모자** (hat)
mo-ja

16) **손님** (guests)
son-nim

생일날 나는 선물을 많이 받았어.
I received a lot of gifts for my birthday.

손님들이 모두 떠났다.
All the guests have left.

그녀는 내게 생일 케이크를 만들어 줬다.
She made me a birthday cake.

HAPPY BIRTHDAY
1
2
3
4
5
6
7
8
9
10
11
12
13
14
15
16

반의어 (OPPOSITES)

1) **깨끗하다** (clean)
kkae-kkeu-ta-da

2) **더럽다** (dirty)
deo-teop-da

3) **적다** (few)
jeok-da

4) **많다** (many)
man-ta

5) **공격하다** (attack)
gong-gyeo-ka-da

6) **방어하다** (defense)
bang-eo-ha-da

7) **똑바르다** (straight)
ttok-ppa-reu-da

8) **구불거리다** (curved)
ku-bul-geo-ri-da

9) **함께** (together)
ham-kke

10) **따로 떨어지다** (separated)
tta-ro tteo-reo-ji-da

11) **어리다, 젊다** (young)
eo-ri-da, jeom-tta

12) **나이가 많다** (old)
na-i-ga man-ta

13) **풍족** (wealth)
pung-jok

14) **부족** (shortage)
bu-jok

15) **오목하다** (concave)
o-mo-ka-da

16) **볼록하다** (convex)
bol-lo-ka-da

테이블 위엔 오렌지가 많이 있다.
There are many oranges on the table.

내가 가장 어리다.
I am the youngest.

이 접시는 더럽다.
This plate is dirty.

13
14
15
16
9
6
5
12
11
10
4
7
8
3
2
1

QUIZ #8

Use arrows to match the corresponding translations:

a. arrival	1. 텐트
b. cheese	2. 인형
c. teddy bear	3. 꽃
d. tourist guide	4. 트럭
e. map	5. 가면
f. fork	6. 치즈
g. grass	7. 사탕
h. candle	8. 공항
i. doll	9. 쌀
j. airport	10. 풀
k. truck	11. 곰 인형
l. flowers	12. 지도
m. tent	13. 도착
n. mask	14. 초
o. rice	15. 관광 가이드
p. candy	16. 포크

Fill in the blank spaces with the options below (use each word only once):

두산 씨와 유민 씨는 지금 _________에 와 있습니다. 결혼 기념일을 맞아서 태국으로 여행을 가기로 했기 때문입니다. 2 시간 후에 ____________가 출발하기 때문에 서둘러서 입국 수속을 밟았습니다. _________을 보여준 후 비행기 표를 발급받았고, _________도 부쳤습니다. 그런 다음에 공항 안에 있는 환전소에 가서 태국 ________로 미리 환전했습니다. 그리고 ______과 차량 대여 예약도 다시 한 번 확인했습니다. 두산 씨와 유민 씨가 ________ 여행하는 게 굉장히 오랜만의 일이라 정말 설렙니다. 빨리 비행기가 ________하기를 몹시 기다리고 있는 중입니다.

공항

현지 통화

호텔

비행기

출발

수하물

여권

함께

CONCLUSION

As you might already know, mastering the massive amount of vocabulary of any language takes a lot of time and effort. Therefore, many linguists and language teachers have suggested numerous ways of learning vocabulary efficiently, and we would like to help you find the way that suits you best. Here we introduce some of the ways that you can take full advantage of this book:

1. Rather than just following the order of the topics set by this book, you can choose whatever you are interested in or whatever you are in need of. If you are in a situation where you can practice the words right after you have learned them, that would be perfect. In doing so, you could avoid feeling bored, and the new words will last in your memory for a longer time.
2. Let's make the best use of the coloring pages. You can color the item every time you finish learning it. Once you find the whole page filled with different colors, it will bring you a lot of joy as well as satisfaction at having mastered the words. Another suggestion regarding the coloring pages is that you can use different tools to paint colors there. For example, you can use color pencils after learning a word of an item, and then for the words you have practiced in real life, you can paint colors again on the colored items with pens of thicker lines and colors. As you know, there is a big difference in learning a word just by using your brain and practicing it by speaking or writing. If you distinguish those words using different coloring methods, you will be motivated to practice them.
3. Make sure to read the transliterations out loud. In the introduction part of this book, you can find the guidelines about some of the principles of the transliteration, so consulting it will help you learn the exact pronunciations. It is helpful to speak them out and write them down in order to retain the words.
4. After checking out most of the words and their transliterations, you should recall the words you have just learned by looking at the pictures only. Repeating this process allows you to remember the massive amount of vocabulary in a very short time.
5. How about guessing the principles of Hangul when reading along the transliterations? Hangul has a phonogram system, which means each character represents a specific sound like in English. Therefore, with a bit of attention you can realize how each character is read. Do not just rely on the transliterations without looking at Hangul, but try to figure out the principles. You will soon grasp the whole system and its principles without any extra effort.
6. This book is designed for individual learners to study on their own, so enjoy the learning process itself and feel the joy out of it!

ANSWERS

QUIZ #1

a-13. b-11. c-10. d-15. e-9. f-12. g-6. h-14. i-8. j-1. k-5. l-2.
m-16. n-7. o-4. p-3.

나의 오늘 하루는 정말 바쁠 것 같다. 오전에 할아버지와 **할머니**를 뵙기로 했기 때문에 일찍부터 준비했다. 난 사랑하고 **존경**하는 조부모님을 오랜만에 뵙게 되어 너무나 **기쁘다**. 할아버지께서 몇 년 전에 **심장** 수술을 받으셨기 때문에 함께 모시고 병원에 갈 것이다.

검사가 끝나면 두 분을 모시고 동물원에 가보려고 한다. 우리 집 근처 동물원에는 코끼리, 사자, 하마 같은 동물들이 있는데, 특히 할머니는 **호랑이**를 좋아하신다. 할아버지는 새를 좋아하시는데, 그 중에서도 **독수리**를 좋아하신다. 저녁에는 두 분께 내 **남자친구**를 소개시켜 드릴 것이다. 그는 얼굴도 잘 생겼지만 무엇보다도 착하고 **친절**하기 때문에 두 분이 마음에 들어 하실 것 같다. 맛있는 저녁 식사를 함께 하며 즐거운 시간을 보낼 것이다.

QUIZ # 2

a-10. b-5. c-8. d-9. e-2. f-13. g-15. h-16. i-3. j-12. k-1. l-4.
m-6. n-7. o-11. p-14.

유민 씨는 오늘 걱정이 많습니다. 친구와 **공원**에서 만나기로 했는데 날씨가 좋지 않기 때문입니다. 일기예보에는 분명히 오늘 날씨가 **화창하다**고 했는데 갑자기 비가 내리기 시작해서 그칠 기미가 보이지 않습니다. 그래서인지 3 월인데도 따뜻하지 않고, 오히려 **춥다**고 느껴집니다.

원래 유민 씨는 **청바지**에 티셔츠를 입고 나가려고 했는데, 비가 오기 때문에 **비옷**을 입어야 하는지 고민 중입니다. 날씨가 좋았다면 한강 공원에서 **자전거 타기**도 할 수 있을 텐데 무척 아쉽습니다.

유민 씨는 추운 날씨를 엄청 싫어해서 빨리 여름이 오기를 바라고 있습니다. 여름이 되면 워터 파크나 **수영장**에도 갈 수 있고 캠핑도 할 수 있기 때문입니다. 다양한 **야외 활동**을 할 수 있어서 유민 씨는 여름을 정말 좋아합니다.

QUIZ # 3

a-16. b-14. c-9. d-8. e-7. f-11. g-3. h-5. i-13. j-12. k-4. l-2.
m-1. n-15. o-6 p-10.

우리 가족은 오늘 집안 대청소를 했어요. 추석 명절이 바로 다음 **주**에 시작하기 때문이죠. 이모와 이모부, 그리고 사촌 동생들과 삼촌네 가족이 오시기 때문에 침대를 정리하고 베개와 **담요**를 여러 개 준비했어요. 욕실에는 샤워 후에 사용할 **수건**도 넉넉히 놓아 두었어요. 치약과 **칫솔**, 샴푸도 새 것으로 바꿔 놓았죠. 우리 엄마는 많은 식구가 먹을 **음식**도 냉장고 안에 넉넉히 사두셨어요. 그리고 **접시**와 숟가락도 많이 필요하죠. 나는 벌써부터 친척들이 우리 집에 올 때가 기대가 돼요. 우리는 같이 거실에 있는 **소파**에 앉아서 재미 있게 얘기도 나누고 **단풍**도 구경하러 갈 거예요.

QUIZ # 4

a-15. b-7. c-9. d-13. e-11. f-10. g-12. h-14. i-8. j-2. k-1. l-3.
m-4. n-5. o-6.

오늘 저녁에는 회사 **동료**의 가족이 우리 집을 방문했다. 그의 아내는 학생들을 가르치고 있는데, 대한 고등학교의 영어 **선생님**이다. 그 부부의 아들은 **축구**를 잘 해서 지금 축구 선수로 활동하고 있다. 날씨가 좋아서 우리는 정원에서 바비큐 파티를 했다. 정원에서 자라고 있는 나무와 **꽃**을 보면서 정원 관리에 대한 얘기를 나누었다. 그리고 서로의 여행담도 주고 받았는데, 동료는 가족 여행으로 제주도에 갔던 얘기를 했다. 제주도의 멋진 절벽과 **폭포** 앞에서 찍은 사진을 보여주기도 했다. 특히 **열기구**를 처음으로 타본 경험을 얘기했는데, 내게도 꼭 한 번 타보라며 추천했다. 우리 가족은 강원도의 **바닷가**에서 찍은 사진을 보여줬다. 다음에는 두 가족이 같이 **산**에 올라가자고 약속했다.

QUIZ # 5

a-7. b-3. c-15 d-13. e-12. f-11. g-2. h-16. i-14. j-8. k-6. l-4.
m-5. n-1. o-10. p-9.

남편과 나는 주말에 시댁을 방문했어요. 시아버님의 **컴퓨터**가 고장이 나서 고쳐 드리러 갔어요. 시부모님께서는 시골에서 농사를 지으면서 살고 계세요. 상추도 심으시고, **옥수수**와 **호박**도 심으시죠. 닭장을 지어 놓고 그 안에서 **암탉**도 여러 마리 키우고 계세요. 몇 년 전에 시골 땅에 직접 집을 짓고 살고 계시는데, 공기도 깨끗하고 밤엔 하늘에 **별**도 많이 보여서 아주 좋아하세요. 시부모님 댁의 동쪽과 북쪽에는 산이 둘러져 있고, 남쪽과 **서쪽**은 탁 트여 있어서 전망도 아주 좋습니다. **피아노** 연주를 들으면서 멀리 산을 바라보고 있으면 멋진 카페에 온 것 같은 느낌이 들어요. 저도 언젠가는 **농부**로서의 삶을 꿈꿉니다.

QUIZ # 6

a-11. b-7. c-9. d-2. e-15. f-14. g-12. h-13. i-10. j-6. k-1. l-8.
m-3. n-4. o-5.

오늘은 정말 기쁜 날이에요. 유민 씨의 동생 유리 씨가 대학교에 **입학**한 날이기 때문이죠. 온 가족이 모여서 맛있는 저녁 식사를 하기로 했습니다. 유리 씨는 생선을 좋아하기 때문에 **고등어** 구이를 할 거예요. 그리고 후라이드 치킨과 **돼지갈비**도 준비했습니다. **후식**으로는 과일을 내놓을 거예요. 유리 씨가 좋아하는 **포도**와 딸기를 미리 사놓았죠. 유리 씨는 대학교에서 경영학을 전공하고 **사업가**가 되고 싶어 해요. 유민 씨는 동생의 꿈을 늘 응원한다고 **편지**에 써서 선물과 함께 줬습니다. 그리고 가족이 모두 이 기쁜 날을 기념하기 위해 핸드폰으로 **사진**도 찍었어요.

QUIZ # 7

a-14. b-11. c-13. d-15. e-12. f-6. g-5. h-1. i-16. j-9. k-4. l-7.
m-10. n-2. o-8. p-3.

여기서 지하철 역으로 가는 길을 알려 드릴게요. 먼저 이 **거리**를 따라 10 분 정도 걸어 가세요. 그럼 **오른쪽**에 공원이 보일 거예요. 거기서 **횡단보도**로 길을 건너세요. 그러고 나서 왼쪽으로 가다 보면 **버스 정류장**이 나와요. 그 근처에는 빵집과 미용실이 있죠. 거기서 두 **블록** 더 가면 지하철 역에 도착합니다. 지하철 역 앞에 큰 **분수대**가 있어서 찾기 쉬울 거예요. 타는 곳은 **에스컬레이터**를 타고 지하 2 **층**까지 가면 돼요.

QUIZ # 8

a-13. b-6. c-11. d-15. e-12. f-16. g-10. h-14. i-2. j-8. k-4. l-3.
m-1. n-5. o-9. p-7.

두산 씨와 유민 씨는 지금 **공항**에 와 있습니다. 결혼 기념일을 맞아서 태국으로 여행을 가기로 했기 때문입니다. 2 시간 후에 **비행기**가 출발하기 때문에 서둘러서 입국 수속을 밟았습니다. **여권**을 보여준 후 비행기 표를 발급받았고, **수하물**도 부쳤습니다. 그런 다음에 공항 안에 있는 환전소에 가서 태국 **현지 통화**로 미리 환전했습니다. 그리고 **호텔**과 차량 대여 예약도 다시 한 번 확인했습니다. 두산 씨와 유민 씨가 **함께** 여행하는 게 굉장히 오랜만의 일이라 정말 설렙니다. 빨리 비행기가 **출발**하기를 몹시 기다리고 있는 중입니다.

Made in the USA
Middletown, DE
05 March 2024